Csaba Balogh

# Greatest
# 551 puzzles

## From practical games
## of 2016

Chess
Evolution

Responsible editor
Csaba Balogh

Cover designer
Piotr Pielach

Typesetting
Piotr Pielach ‹www.i-press.pl›

First edition 2017 by Chess Evolution

*Greatest 551 puzzles. From practical games of 2016*
Copyright © 2017 Chess Evolution

ISBN: 978-83-945362-5-1

All sales or enquiries should be directed to Chess Evolution
2040 Budaors, Nyar utca 16, Hungary

e-mail: info@chess-evolution.com
website: www.chess-evolution.com

Printed in Hungary

# TABLE OF CONTENTS

# KEY TO SYMBOLS

| | |
|---|---|
| = | Equality or equal chances |
| ⩲ | White has a slight advantage |
| ⩱ | Black has a slight advantage |
| ± | White is better |
| ∓ | Black is better |
| +- | White has a decisive advantage |
| -+ | Black has a decisive advantage |
| ∞ | unclear |
| ⯦ | with compensation |
| ⇆ | with counterplay |
| ↑ | with initiative |
| → | with an attack |
| Δ | with the idea |
| □ | only move |
| | |
| N | novelty |
| ! | a good move |
| !! | an excellent move |
| ? | a weak move |
| ?? | a blunder |
| !? | an interesing move |
| ?! | a dubious move |
| + | check |
| # | mate |

# PREFACE

As a professional chess player, I know exactly how important it is to perform well in tactical calculations. We face them so often that after playing a great game, we can simply blunder something and throw away a safe point, causing ourself sleepless nights!

For most of the players and chess fans, the biggest pleasure in a chessgame is to beat an opponent with a beautiful combination, of which we can be proud at. However to live with all the given oportunities and not miss any of the chances, we must stay in sharp shape all the time, what we can reach only by practicing puzzlesolving.

Many puzzle books are based on artificial positions or selected only for their beauty. The concept of my book is different. The highest priority is to "**use the practical side of the puzzles" and take the level of calculation to a completely new dimension.**

All the puzzles have been selected from recent games, trying to put the reader in the shoes of "the player".

The difficulty of the different sections might also give you a right evaluation of your current tactical skills and bring them further ahead.

I tried to mix three things in my book:
      1. a lot of fun in solving the puzzles,
      2. a lot of different tactical ideas,
      3. and of course, the direct practical use for your future games.

A very important factor to keep in mind — all the **practical motifs from the book can definitely be used in your future games!**

Enjoy!

Csaba Balogh

# INTRODUCTION

## USEFUL INFORMATION FOR OUR DEAR READERS

This book is the continuation of the successful puzzle-book series, which started with the "Greatest 365 Puzzles" and "Greatest 501 Puzzles" from 2012. It was followed by „Tactics, Tactics, Tactics!" Volumes 3 and 4 which covered the best practical puzzles of 2013-2015.

The new book contains 551 puzzles divided into 3 chapters. You will find a huge range of tactical ideas that you can use in your own games! All the puzzles have been collected from practical games throughout 2016. In each section the puzzles are sorted according to the date of the game.

The book consists of three chapters:
1. **Easy (217 Puzzles)**
2. **Medium (188 Puzzles)**
3. **Hard (146 Puzzles)**

All-in-all, 551 puzzles created by the greatest masters of our time, such as Carlsen, Caruana, Kramnik, Anand and many more.

I advise you to try to solve all the combinations in each chapter one-by-one, because a less difficult solution from the „Easy" section might be even more brilliant from the beauty point of view than a ‚nutcracker' from the „Hard" ones. Even if a puzzle can be easily solved, it sharpens your tactical skills and makes it so much easier to find such solutions in a practical game, even under difficult circumstances.

To be tactically sharp is one of the basic requirements for a successful chess player!

## (1)

▷ E. Sveshnikov
► N. Vitiugov
Keres memorial rapid, 2016.01.08

1... −+

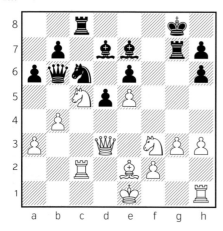

## (2)

▷ Y. Krupenski
► M. Matlakov
Keres memorial rapid, 2016.01.08

1... -+

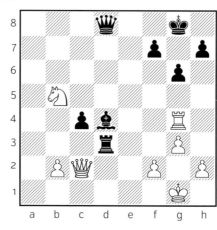

## (3)

▷ B. Gelfand
► I. Zhuk
Keres memorial rapid, 2016.01.08

1. +-

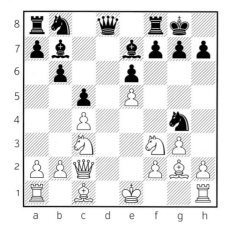

## (4)

▷ V. Sveshnikov
► N. Vitiugov
Keres memorial rapid, 2016.01.10

1... -+

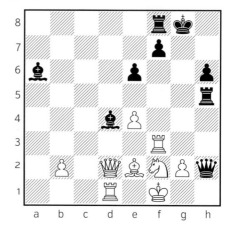

## (5)

▷ **K. Miton**
► **T. Kantans**
Keres memorial rapid, 2016.01.10

1. +−

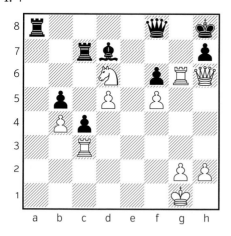

## (6)

▷ **D. Lintchevski**
► **E. Sutovsky**
Keres memorial rapid, 2016.01.10

1... −+

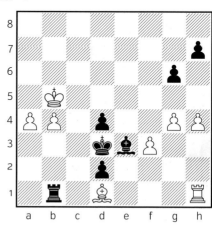

## (7)

▷ **M. Noble**
► **Ma Qun**
New Zealand rapid, 2016.01.11

1... −+

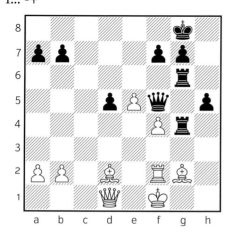

## (8)

▷ **A. Czebe**
► **I. Popov**
Delhi Open, 2016.01.12

1... −+

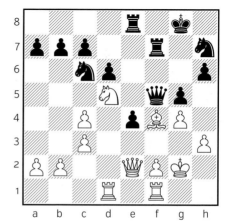

## (9)

▷ **B. Adhiban**
▶ **N. Abasov**
Wijk aan Zee B, 2016.01.16

1. +-

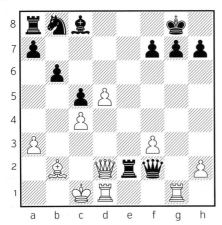

## (10)

▷ **K. Raghunandan**
▶ **V. Bernardskiy**
Chennai Open, 2016.01.19

1... -+

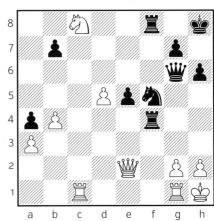

## (11)

▷ **S. Sevian**
▶ **B. Bok**
Wijk aan Zee B, 2016.01.23

1... =

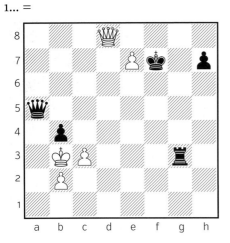

## (12)

▷ **B. Adhiban**
▶ **A. Dreev**
Wijk aan Zee B, 2016.01.23

1. +-

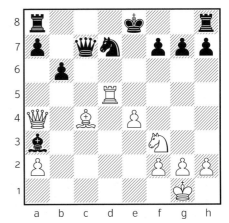

## (13)

▷ E. Nakar
► D. Jakovenko
Gibraltar Open, 2016.01.27

1... -+

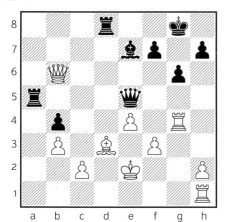

## (14)

▷ G. Jones
► P. Carlsson
Gibraltar Open, 2016.01.27

1. +-

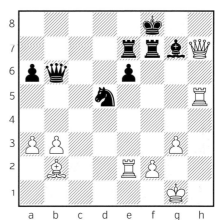

## (15)

▷ M. Esserman
► E. Iturrizaga
Gibraltar Open, 2016.01.27

1... -+

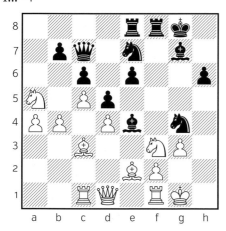

## (16)

▷ F. Perez Ponsa
► R. Wojtaszek
Gibraltar Open, 2016.02.01

1... -+

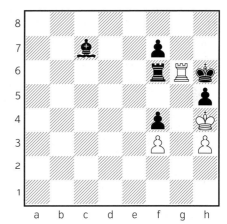

## (17)

▷ **R. Padmini**
▶ **M. Al Sayed**
Gibraltar Open, 2016.02.01

1. +-

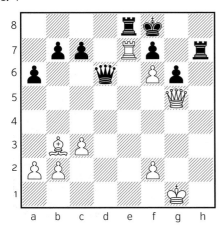

## (18)

▷ **P. Harikrishna**
▶ **S. Vidit**
Gibraltar Open, 2016.02.02

1. +-

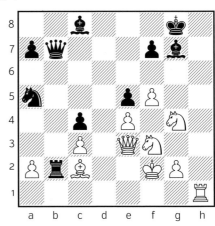

## (19)

▷ **R. Edouard**
▶ **V. Gunina**
Gibraltar Open, 2016.02.02

1. +-

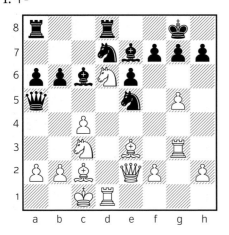

## (20)

▷ **A. Donchenko**
▶ **M. Esserman**
Gibraltar Open, 2016.02.03

1. +-

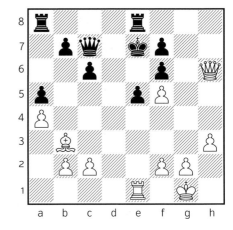

## (21)

▷ A. Schenk
► M. Bartel
German league, 2016.02.06

1... -+

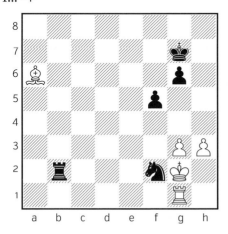

## (22)

▷ B. Gelfand
► A. Morozevich
Zurich, 2016.02.13

1. +-

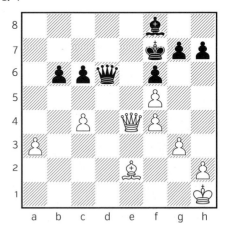

## (23)

▷ L. Aronian
► A. Shirov
Zurich blitz, 2016.02.15

1. +-

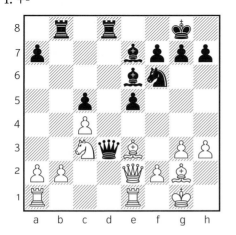

## (24)

▷ V. Anand
► H. Nakamura
Zurich blitz, 2016.02.15

1. +-

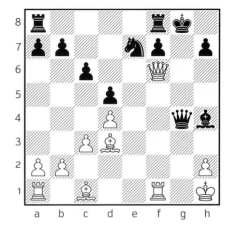

## (25)

▷ A. Gupta
► C. Sochacki
Cappelle la Grande, 2016.02.16

1. +-

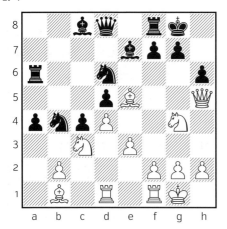

## (26)

▷ C. Bauer
► V. Burmakin
Cappelle la Grande, 2016.02.16

1. +-

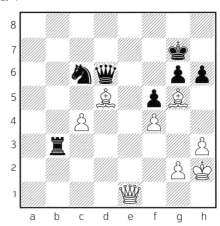

## (27)

▷ S. Khademalsharieh
► V. Gunina
Tehran WGP, 2016.02.18

1. +-

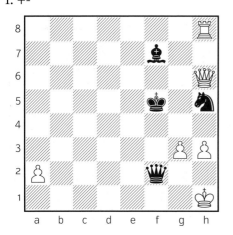

## (28)

▷ N. Batsiashvili
► V. Gunina
Tehran WGP, 2016.02.19

1... -+

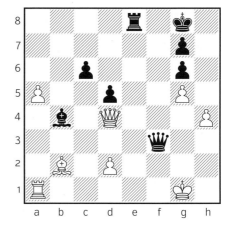

## (29)

▷ **M. Rodshtein**
► **M. Tazbir**
German league, 2016.02.20

1. +-

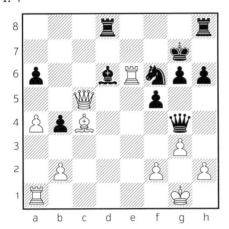

## (30)

▷ **H. Koneru**
► **A. Stefanova**
Tehran WGP, 2016.02.23

1. +-

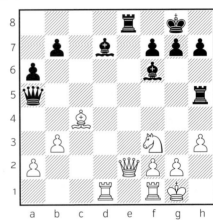

## (31)

▷ **Wang Hao**
► **L. Dominguez**
IMSA blitz, 2016.02.28

1... -+

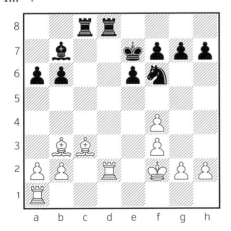

## (32)

▷ **P. Harikrishna**
► **D. Navara**
IMSA blitz, 2016.02.29

1. +-

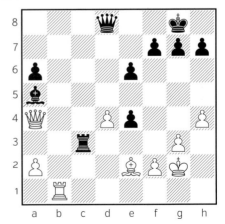

### (33)

▷ **Wang Hao**
► **E. Tomashevsky**
IMSA blitz, 2016.03.01

1... =

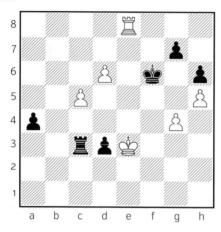

### (34)

▷ **R. Mamedov**
► **Wang Hao**
IMSA blitz, 2016.03.01

1... -+

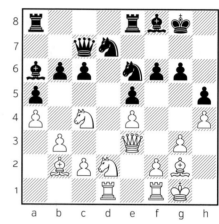

### (35)

▷ **V. Ivanchuk**
► **G. Sargissian**
IMSA blitz, 2016.03.01

1. +-

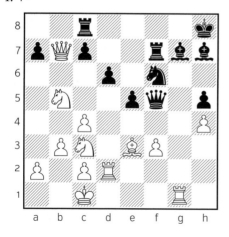

### (36)

▷ **L. Dominguez**
► **S. Mamedyarov**
IMSA blitz, 2016.03.01

1. +-

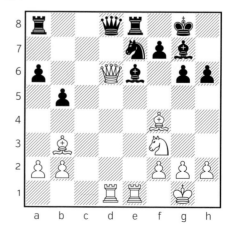

## (37)

▷ D. Navara
► S. Mamedyarov
IMSA rapid, 2016.03.03

1. +-

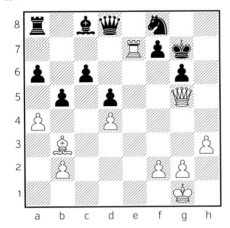

## (38)

▷ L. Dominguez
► L. Fressinet
IMSA rapid, 2016.03.03

1. +-

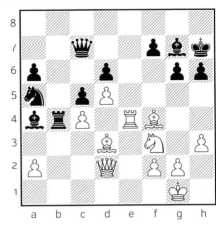

## (39)

▷ C. Aravindh
► A. Motylev
Aeroflot Open, 2016.03.09

1... -+

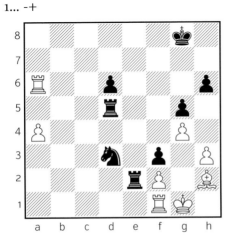

## (40)

▷ A. Moiseenko
► B. Socko
German league, 2016.03.13

1... -+

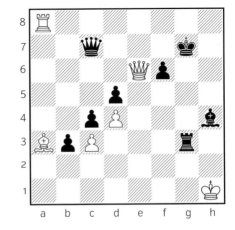

## (41)

▷ **G. Popilski**
► **R. Li**
Dallas, 2016.03.15

1... -+

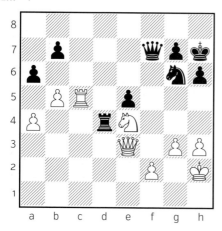

## (42)

▷ **H. Gretarsson**
► **J. Lind**
Reykjavik Open, 2016.03.15

1. +-

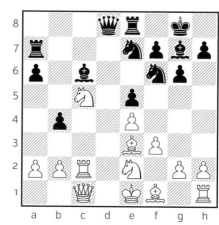

## (43)

▷ **M. Sadler**
► **S. Chow**
4NCL, 2016.03.19

1. +-

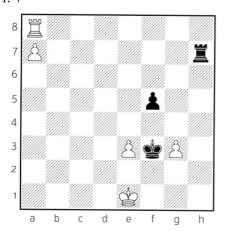

## (44)

▷ **N. Pert**
► **R. Williamson**
4NCL, 2016.03.19

1. +-

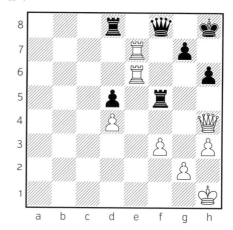

## (45)

▷ **Ni Hua**
► **M. Wecker**
Grenke Open, 2016.03.24

1. +-

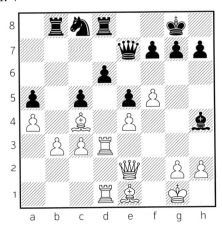

## (46)

▷ **H. Melkumyan**
► **B. Atzmon Simon**
Doeberl Cup, 2016.03.24

1. +-

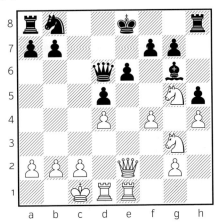

## (47)

▷ **J. Ikeda**
► **S. Ganguly**
Doeberl Cup, 2016.03.25

1... -+

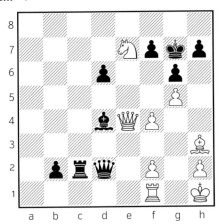

## (48)

▷ **T. Beerdsen**
► **Li Chao**
Grenke Open, 2016.03.25

1... -+

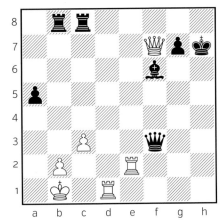

# (49)

▷ S. Vidit
► I. Saeed
Asian Nations Cup, 2016.03.31

1. +-

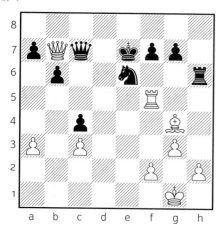

# (50)

▷ D. Milanovic
► K. Georgiev
Karpos Open, 2016.04.04

1... -+

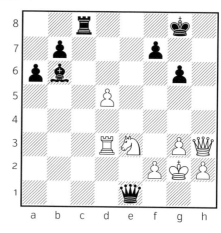

# (51)

▷ T. Nedev
► R. Markus
Karpos Open, 2016.04.05

1... -+

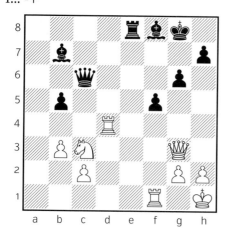

# (52)

▷ L. Miron
► M. Parligras
Romanian Champ., 2016.04.05

1... -+

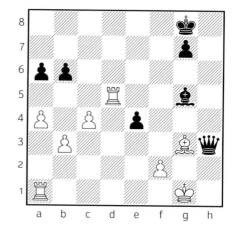

## (53)

▷ **E. Hossein**
► **M. Mosadeghpour**
Asian Nations Cup, 2016.04.05

1... -+

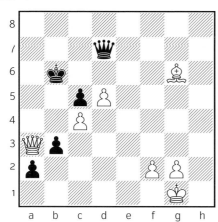

## (54)

▷ **M. Santos Ruiz**
► **T. Gareev**
Colin Crouch Masters, 2016.04.06

1... -/+

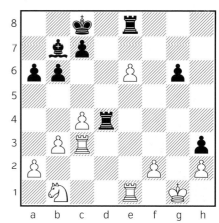

## (55)

▷ **A. Bezgodov**
► **I. Lysyj**
Sergievskiy Mem. Rapid, 2016.04.11

1. +-

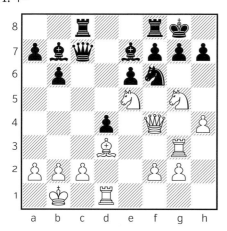

## (56)

▷ **H. Nakamura**
► **S. Shankland**
us Championship, 2016.04.18

1. +-

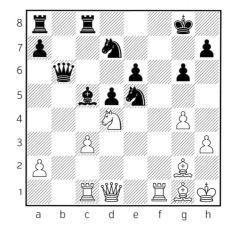

## (57)

▷ A. Giri
► P. Eljanov
Norway blitz, 2016.04.18

1. +−

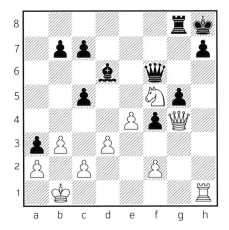

## (58)

▷ S. Zhigalko
► M. Petrosyan
Gaprindashvili Cup, 2016.04.28

1. +−

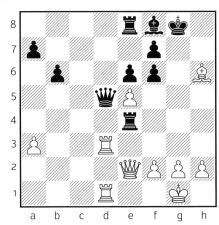

## (59)

▷ D. Dubov
► V. Yandemirov
Russian league, 2016.05.03

1. +−

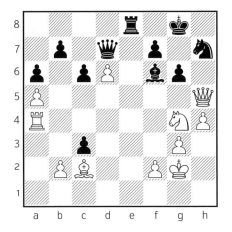

## (60)

▷ A. Korobov
► V. Yandemirov
Russian league, 2016.05.06

1. +−

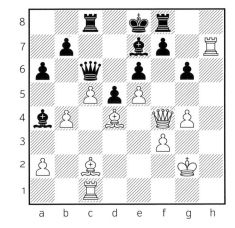

## (61)

▷ M. Samusenko
► I. Popov
Russian league, 2016.05.08

1... -+

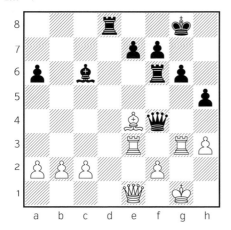

## (62)

▷ C. Lupulescu
► M. Godena
European Championship, 2016.05.13

1. +-

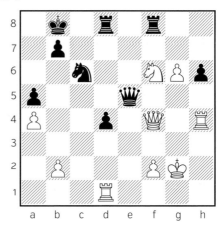

## (63)

▷ K. Kulaots
► A. Moiseenko
European Championship, 2016.05.13

1. +-

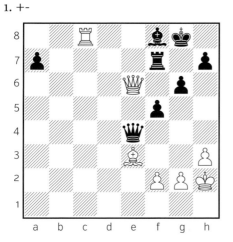

## (64)

▷ S. Zhigalko
► A. Boruchovsky
European Championship, 2016.05.14

1. +-

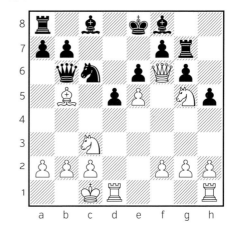

## (65)

▷ **F. Vallejo Pons**
▶ **M. Palac**
European Championship, 2016.05.14

1. +-

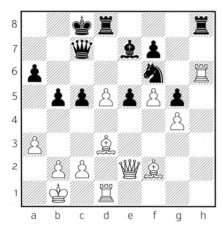

## (66)

▷ **M. Ragger**
▶ **S. Ter Sahakyan**
European Championship, 2016.05.17

1... -+

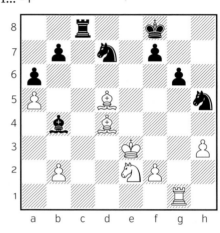

## (67)

▷ **B. Jobava**
▶ **E. Inarkiev**
European Championship, 2016.05.17

1... =

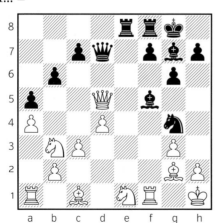

## (68)

▷ **A. Ipatov**
▶ **H. Stefansson**
European Championship, 2016.05.17

1. +-

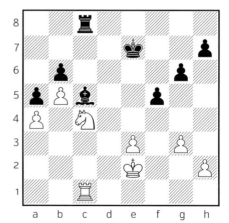

## (69)

▷ **D. Nisipeanu**
► **Z. Kozul**
European Championship, 2016.05.19

1. +-

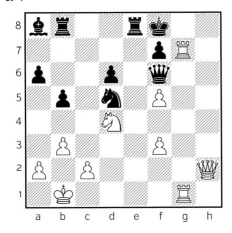

## (70)

▷ **R. Hovhannisyan**
► **J. Stocek**
European Championship, 2016.05.19

1. +-

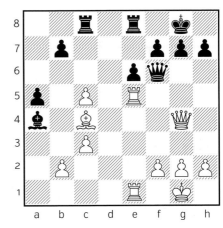

## (71)

▷ **S. Movsesian**
► **A. Shomoev**
Kurnosov memorial, 2016.05.27

1. +-

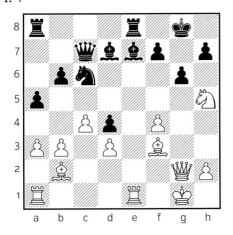

## (72)

▷ **S. Sethuraman**
► **D. Sengupta**
Asian Continental, 2016.05.30

1. +-

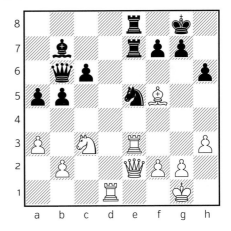

# (73)

▷ H. Stevic
► O. Letreguilly
French league, 2016.06.01

1. +−

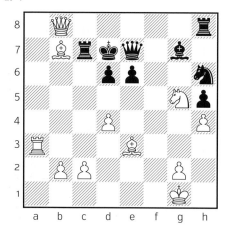

# (74)

▷ K. Oliva
► I. Morovic Fernandez
American Continental, 2016.06.01

1... −+

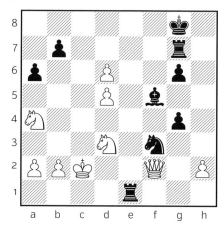

# (75)

▷ A. Moskalenko
► A. Aleksandrov
Nezhmetdinov memorial, 2016.06.02

1. +−

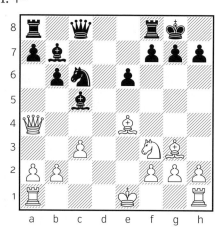

# (76)

▷ R. Ponomariov
► N. Short
Neoclassical Masters Rapid, 2016.06.03

1. +−

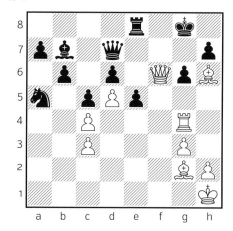

## (77)

▷ **I. Ortiz Suarez**
► **S. Barrientos**
American Continental, 2016.06.03

1... -+

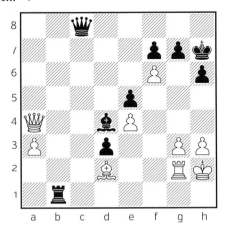

## (78)

▷ **S. Mareco**
► **D. Flores**
American Cont. Tiebreak, 2016.06.05

1... -+

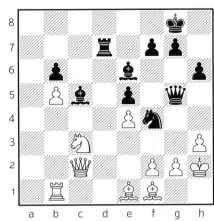

## (79)

▷ **V. Kramnik**
► **M. Carlsen**
Grand tour, Paris blitz, 2016.06.11

1... -+

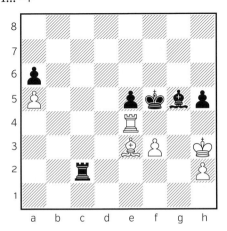

## (80)

▷ **A. Giri**
► **L. Fressinet**
Grand tour, Paris blitz, 2016.06.12

1. +-

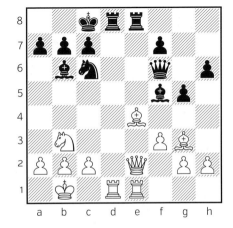

# (81)

▷ **M. Carlsen**
► **F. Caruana**
Grand tour, Leuven rapid, 2016.06.17

1... -+

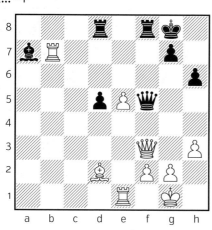

# (82)

▷ **P. Svidler**
► **M. Kazhgaleyev**
Eurasian Blitz Champ., 2016.06.18

1. +-

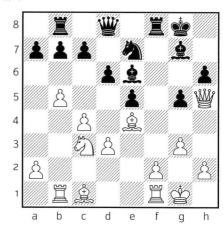

# (83)

▷ **V. Onischuk**
► **S. Karjakin**
Eurasian blitz, 2016.06.18

1... -+

# (84)

▷ **Le Quang Liem**
► **D. Makhnyov**
Eurasian Blitz Champ., 2016.06.18

1. +-

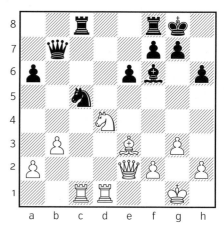

## (85)

▷ I. Gaponenko
► A. Dreev
Eurasian Blitz Champ., 2016.06.18

1... -+

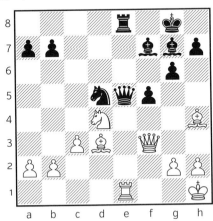

## (86)

▷ O. Dzyuban
► I. Saric
Eurasian Blitz Champ., 2016.06.18

1... -+

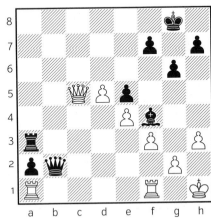

## (87)

▷ O. Dzyuban
► I. Saric
Eurasian Blitz Champ., 2016.06.18

1... -+

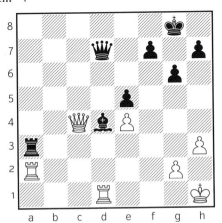

## (88)

▷ I. Nepomniachtchi
► A. Aleksandrov
Eurasian Blitz, 2016.06.19

1. +-

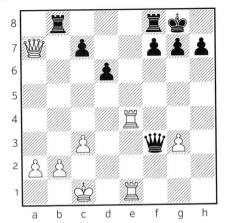

## (89)

▷ **W. So**
► **V. Kramnik**
Grand tour, Leuven blitz, 2016.06.20

1... -+

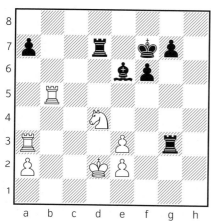

## (90)

▷ **V. Sviridov**
► **V. Fedoseev**
Russian Higher league, 2016.06.22

1... -+

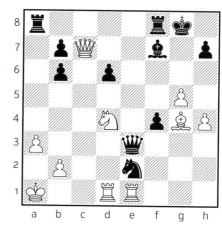

## (91)

▷ **A. Riazantsev**
► **A. Predke**
Russian Higher league, 2016.06.22

1. =

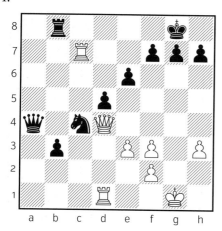

## (92)

▷ **M. Carlsen**
► **T. Petrosian**
Internet blitz, 2016.06.23

1. +-

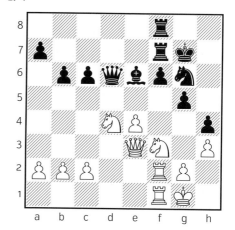

# (93)

▷ **M. Vavulin**
▶ **G. Oparin**
Russian Higher league, 2016.06.25

1... -+

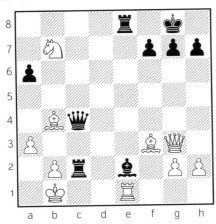

# (94)

▷ **I. Bocharov**
▶ **D. Kurberinov**
Russian Higher league, 2016.06.25

1. +-

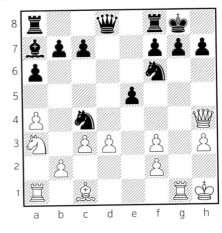

# (95)

▷ **M. Oganian**
▶ **I. Khairullin**
Russian Higher league, 2016.06.27

1... -+

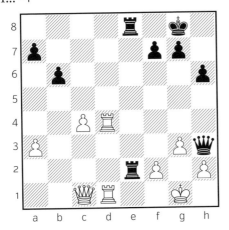

# (96)

▷ **K. Alekseenko**
▶ **S. Lobanov**
Russian Higher league, 2016.06.27

1. +-

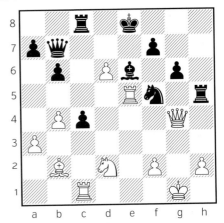

## (97)

▷ **A. Sarana**
► **S. Volkov**
Russian Higher league, 2016.06.28

1... -+

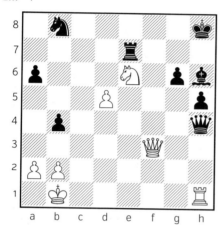

## (98)

▷ **L. Lenic**
► **J. Skoberne**
Vidmar memorial, 2016.06.28

1. +-

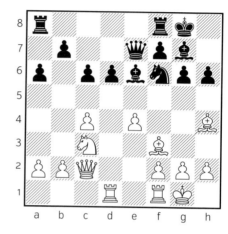

## (99)

▷ **D. Kokarev**
► **K. Alekseenko**
Russian Higher league, 2016.06.28

1. +-

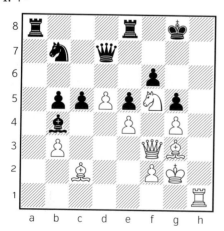

## (100)

▷ **N. Capone**
► **G. Jones**
Porticcio Open, 2016.06.30

1... -+

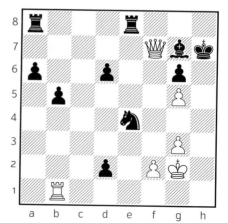

# (101)

▷ **D. Khismatullin**
▶ **A. Gabrielian**
Russian Higher league, 2016.07.01

1. +-

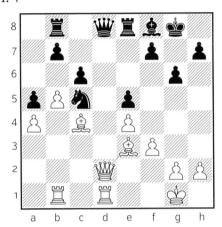

# (102)

▷ **D. Dubov**
▶ **V. Sviridov**
Russian Higher league, 2016.07.01

1. +-

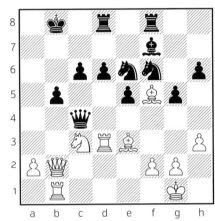

# (103)

▷ **A. Shimanov**
▶ **Y. Zherebukh**
Annual World Open, 2016.07.04

1. +-

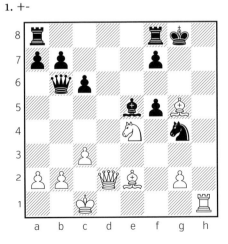

# (104)

▷ **G. Arnaudov**
▶ **I. Saric**
Greek league, 2016.07.05

1... -+

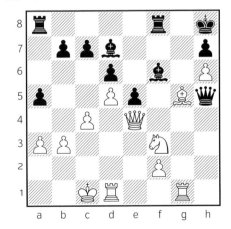

# (105)

▷ **B. Veltkamp**
► **E. Alekseev**
Amsterdam Open, 2016.07.09

1... -+

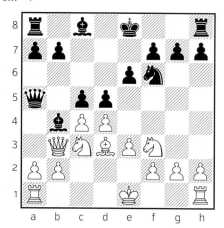

# (106)

▷ **E. Najer**
► **R. Buhmann**
Dortmund, 2016.07.09

1. +-

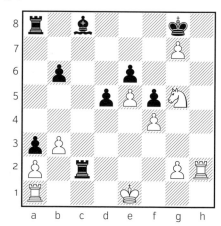

# (107)

▷ **P. Harikrishna**
► **Ding Liren**
Danzhou, 2016.07.10

1. +-

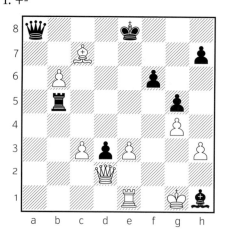

# (108)

▷ **Bu Xiangzhi**
► **V. Ivanchuk**
Danzhou, 2016.07.10

1. +-

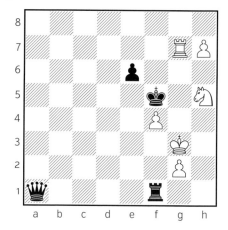

## (109)

▷ **M. Bartel**
▶ **B. Lalith**
Najdorf memorial, 2016.07.10

1. +-

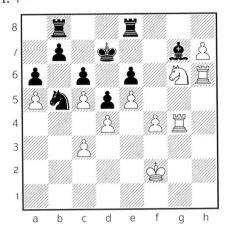

## (110)

▷ **A. Areshchenko**
▶ **A. Fier**
Najdorf memorial, 2016.07.13

1. +-

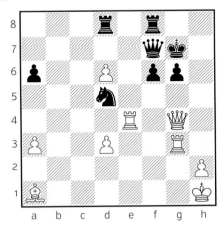

## (111)

▷ **E. Najer**
▶ **M. Vachier Lagrave**
Dortmund, 2016.07.15

1... -+

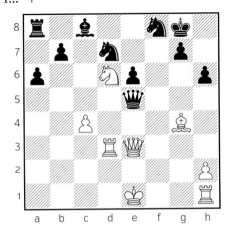

## (112)

▷ **B. Savchenko**
▶ **P. Gelazonia**
Aleksandria Cup, 2016.07.16

1. +-

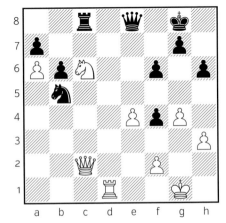

## (113)

▷ **A. Gupta**
► **A. Smirnov**
Najdorf memorial, 2016.07.16

1. +-

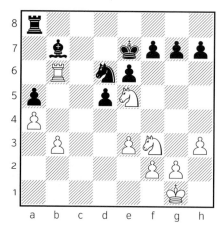

## (114)

▷ **M. Carlsen**
► **A. Giri**
Bilbao, 2016.07.22

1. +-

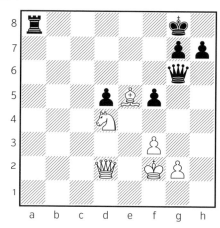

## (115)

▷ **V. Ivanchuk**
► **S. Mamedyarov**
Turkish league, 2016.07.30

1. +-

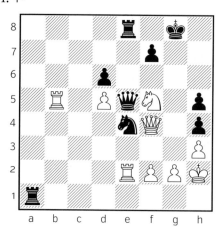

## (116)

▷ **Yu Lie**
► **Zhao Jun**
Chinese league, 2016.07.31

1. +-

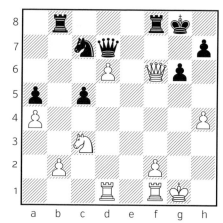

## (117)

▷ N. Vitiugov
► A. Kovchan
Biel Open, 2016.07.31

1. +-

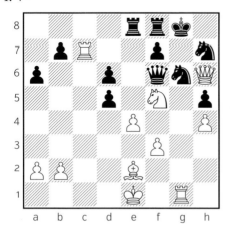

## (118)

▷ K. Sasikiran
► M. Al Sayed
Biel Open, 2016.08.02

1. +-

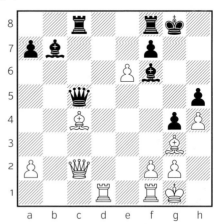

## (119)

▷ A. Fier
► O. Romanishin
Fano Open, 2016.08.04

1. +-

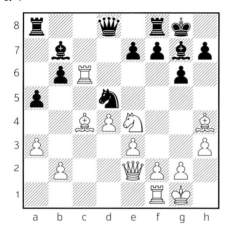

## (120)

▷ M. Vachier Lagrave
► V. Anand
Sinquefield Cup, 2016.08.06

1... -+

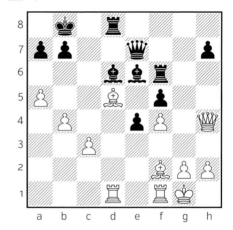

## (121)

▷ J. Xiong
► C. Menezes
World Juniors, 2016.08.09

1. +-

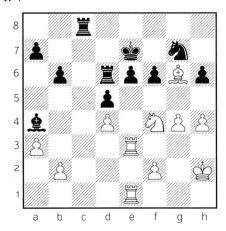

## (122)

▷ V. Topalov
► Ding Liren
Sinquefield Cup, 2016.08.09

1. +-

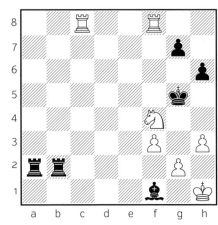

## (123)

▷ S. Gagare
► B. Ivekovic
World Juniors, 2016.08.09

1... -+

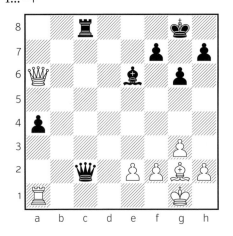

## (124)

▷ K. Sasikiran
► I. Sukandar
Vlissingen Open, 2016.08.10

1. +-

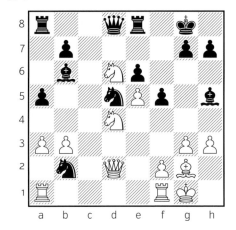

## (125)

▷ C. Menezes
► Q. Yuan
World Juniors, 2016.08.14

1. +−

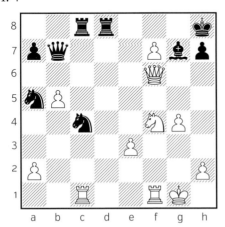

## (126)

▷ E. Rozentalis
► L. Johansson
Manhem GM, 2016.08.18

1. +−

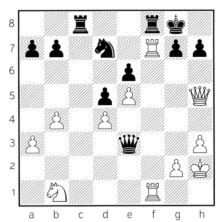

## (127)

▷ J. Degraeve.
► V. Veys
French Championship, 2016.08.21

1. +−

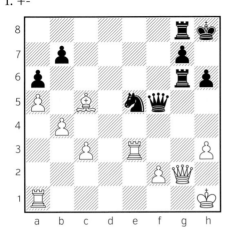

## (128)

▷ M. Swayams
► B. Adhiban
Abu Dhabi Open, 2016.08.22

1... −+

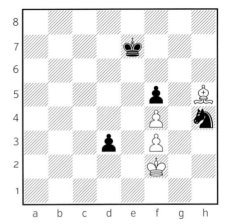

## (129)

▷ **V. Petkov**
▶ **E. Cordova**
Spanish league, 2016.08.22

1. +−

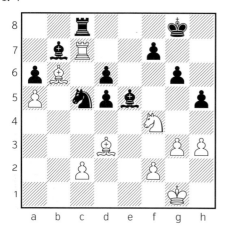

## (130)

▷ **H. Melkumyan**
▶ **T. Ravi**
Abu Dhabi Open, 2016.08.22

1. +−

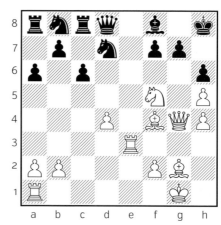

## (131)

▷ **Y. Fang**
▶ **Y. Wei**
Chinese Rapid Champ., 2016.08.25

1... −+

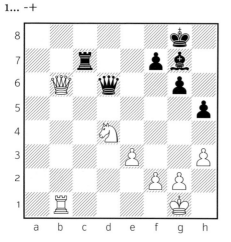

## (132)

▷ **S. Sevian**
▶ **R. Panjwani**
US Masters, 2016.08.26

1. +−

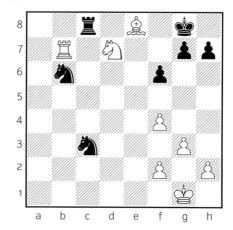

## (133)

▷ S. Vidit
► L. Aguilar
Olympiad, 2016.09.02

1. +-

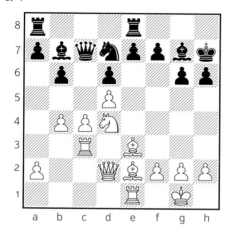

## (134)

▷ V. Topalov
► S. Nadir
Olympiad, 2016.09.02

1. +-

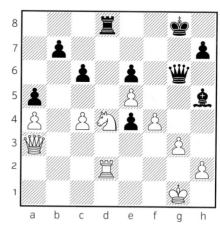

## (135)

▷ D. Navara
► P. Eljanov
Olympiad, 2016.09.02

1... -+

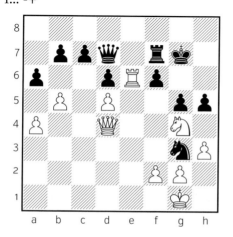

## (136)

▷ L. Fressinet
► W. Lorenzana
Olympiad, 2016.09.02

1. +-

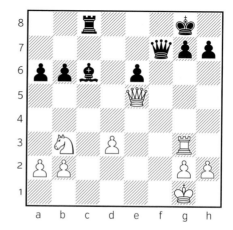

## (137)

▷ **Y. Atabayev**
► **V. Kramnik**
Olympiad, 2016.09.03

1... -+

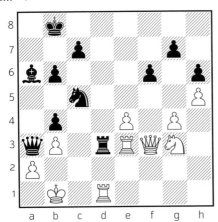

## (138)

▷ **B. Adhiban**
► **S. Minero Pineda**
Olympiad, 2016.09.03

1. +-

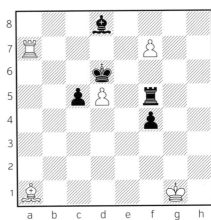

## (139)

▷ **D. Svetushkin**
► **I. Nepomniachtchi**
Olympiad, 2016.09.04

1... -+

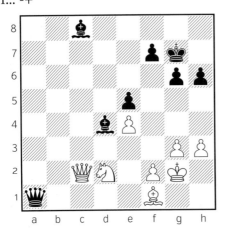

## (140)

▷ **D. Jakovenko**
► **I. Popov**
Moscow blitz, 2016.09.04

1. +-

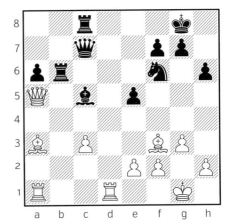

## (141)

▷ **J. Cubas**
► **K. Stupak**
Olympiad, 2016.09.04

1... -+

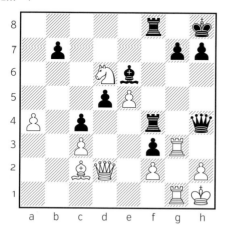

## (142)

▷ **F. Caruana**
► **F. Peralta**
Olympiad, 2016.09.04

1. +-

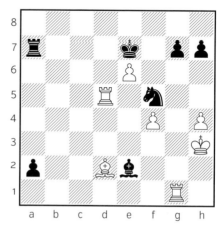

## (143)

▷ **J. Pineda**
► **F. Berkes**
Olympiad, 2016.09.05

1... -+

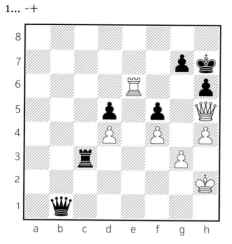

## (144)

▷ **L'E. Ami**
► **D. Howell**
Olympiad, 2016.09.05

1. +-

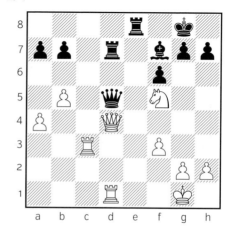

## (145)

▷ **B. Bok**
► **G. Jones**
Olympiad, 2016.09.05

1. +-

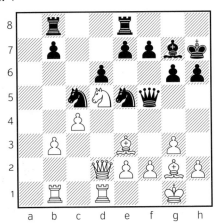

## (146)

▷ **A. Brkic**
► **B. Kalezic**
Olympiad, 2016.09.06

1. +-

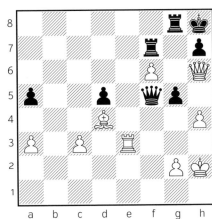

## (147)

▷ **M. Kolago**
► **Y. Vovk**
Polish league, 2016.09.07

1... -+

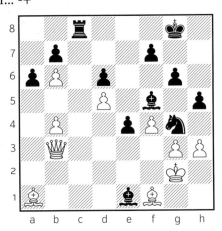

## (148)

▷ **T. Nedev**
► **F. Amonatov**
Olympiad, 2016.09.08

1... -+

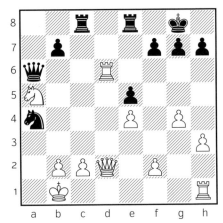

# (149)

▷ M. Kazhgaleyev
► A. Neiksans
Olympiad, 2016.09.08

1... -+

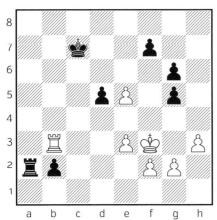

# (150)

▷ E. Hansen
► A. Zhigalko
Olympiad, 2016.09.08

1. +-

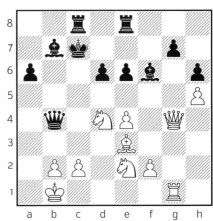

# (151)

▷ E. Hossain
► I. Ivanisevic
Olympiad, 2016.09.09

1. +-

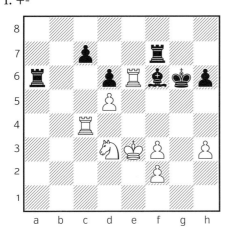

# (152)

▷ A. Mijovic
► V. Cmilyte
Olympiad Women, 2016.09.10

1... -+

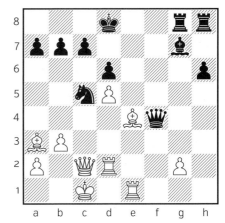

## (153)

▷ S. Mareco
► J. Sadorra
Olympiad, 2016.09.11

1... -+

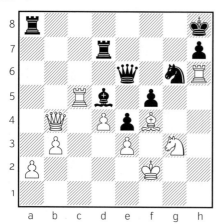

## (154)

▷ V. Laznicka
► L'E. Ami
Olympiad, 2016.09.11

1. +-

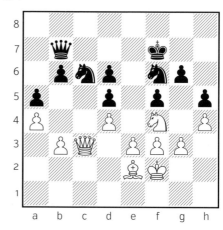

## (155)

▷ P. Harikrishna
► S. Karjakin
Olympiad, 2016.09.12

1. +-

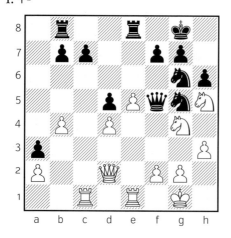

## (156)

▷ M. Carlsen
► E. Ghaem Maghami
Olympiad, 2016.09.12

1. +-

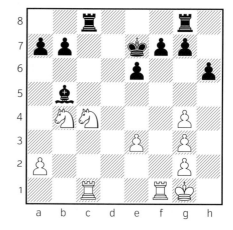

# (157)

▷ E. Hansen
► S. Shankland
Olympiad, 2016.09.13

1. +-

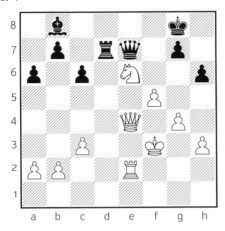

# (158)

▷ E. Inarkiev
► Hou Yifan
Rapid match, 2016.09.17

1... -+

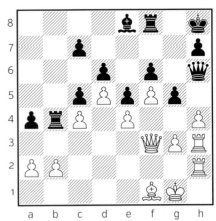

# (159)

▷ Hou Yifan
► E. Inarkiev
Rapid match, 2016.09.17

1. +-

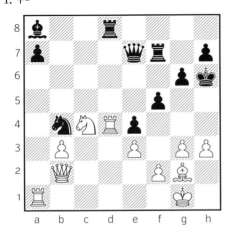

# (160)

▷ B. Grachev
► E. Kretov
Moscow Rapid, 2016.09.17

1. +-

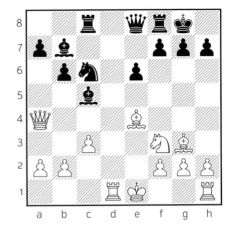

## (161)

▷ **R. Rapport**
► **M. Antipov**
Spanish league, 2016.09.27

1. +-

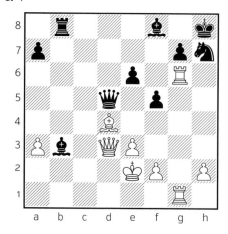

## (162)

▷ **E. Romanov**
► **R. Hasangatin**
Russian Rapid Champ., 2016.10.02

1. +-

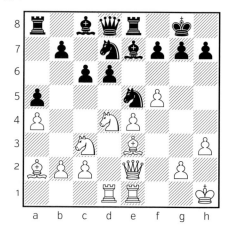

## (163)

▷ **A. Rakhamov**
► **P. Ponkratov**
Russian Rapid Champ., 2016.10.02

1. +-

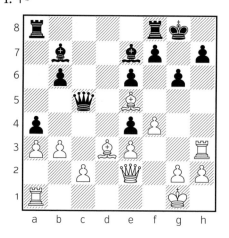

## (164)

▷ **D. Dubov**
► **V. Zakhartsov**
Russian Rapid Champ., 2016.10.02

1. +-

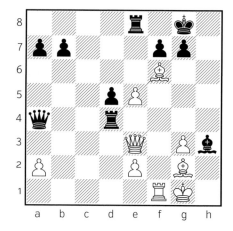

## (165)

▷ **S. Vidit**
▶ **B. Lalith**
Isle of Man, 2016.10.05

1. +−

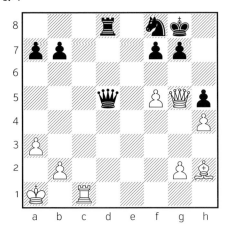

## (166)

▷ **A. Morozevich**
▶ **G. Kamsky**
Russian Rapid league, 2016.10.05

1. +−

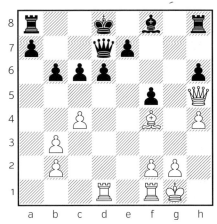

## (167)

▷ **F. Caruana**
▶ **S. Movsesian**
Isle of Man, 2016.10.05

1. +/−

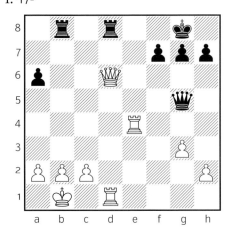

## (168)

▷ **A. Alexeev**
▶ **V. Bologan**
Russian Rapid league, 2016.10.05

1. +−

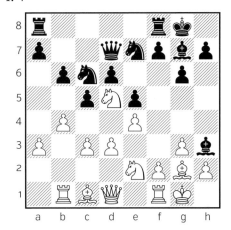

## (169)

▷ A. Karpov
► J. Timman
Basamro match, 2016.10.08

1... -/+

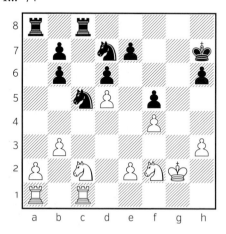

## (170)

▷ P. Wallace
► A. Salem
Isle of Man, 2016.10.09

1... -+

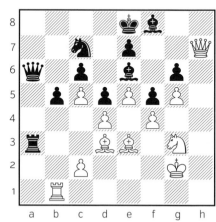

## (171)

▷ I. Cheparinov
► S. Bekker Jensen
Croatian league, 2016.10.09

1. +-

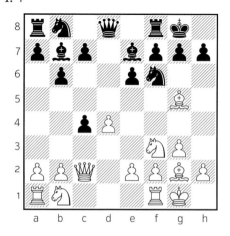

## (172)

▷ I. Cheparinov
► Z. Kozul
Croatian league, 2016.10.16

1. +-

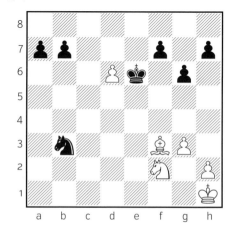

## (173)

▷ M. Adams
► S. Kindermann
German league, 2016.10.16

1. +/-

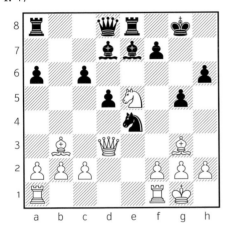

## (174)

▷ D. Jakovenko
► A. Goganov
Russian Championship, 2016.10.17

1... -+

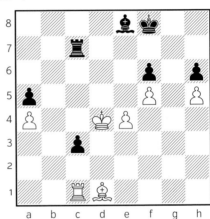

## (175)

▷ V. Artemiev
► O. Biriukov
Chigorin memorial, 2016.10.20

1. +-

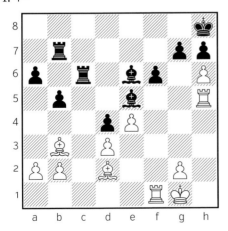

## (176)

▷ D. Navara
► K. Bulski
Slovakian league, 2016.10.22

1. +-

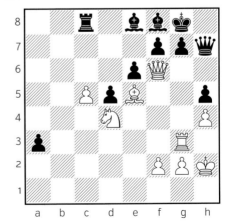

## (177)

▷ **T. Gharamian**
► **D. Vocaturo**
Corsican Circuit, 2016.10.27

1. +-

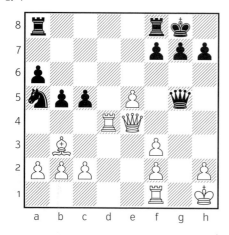

## (178)

▷ **D. Bocharov**
► **E. Tomashevsky**
Russian Championship, 2016.10.27

1... -+

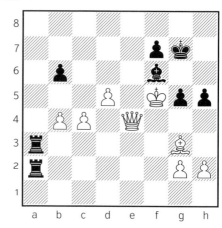

## (179)

▷ **A. Korobov**
► **Hou Yifan**
Corsican Circuit, 2016.10.28

1. +-

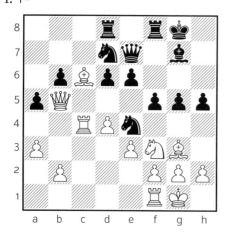

## (180)

▷ **T. Nabaty**
► **B. Murtazin**
Karadzica memorial, 2016.10.30

1. +-

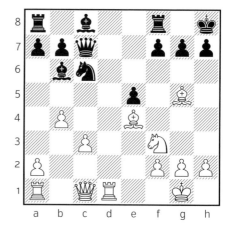

## (181)

▷ **Yu Yangyi**
▶ **Wang Yue**
Chinese league, 2016.10.31

1. +-

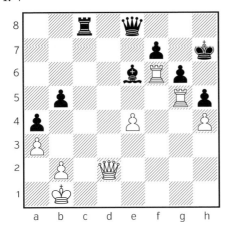

## (182)

▷ **T. Nabaty**
▶ **J. Skoberne**
Karadzica memorial, 2016.11.01

1. +-

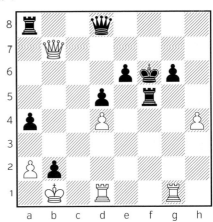

## (183)

▷ **D. Komarov**
▶ **A. Fier**
Payakht Cup, 2016.11.01

1. +-

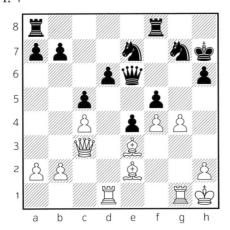

## (184)

▷ **E. Torre**
▶ **B. Damljanovic**
Suleymanpasa GM, 2016.11.05

1. +-

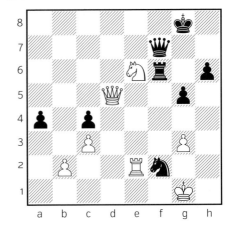

## (185)

▷ T. Luther
► S. Danailov
Suleymanpasa GM, 2016.11.05

1. +-

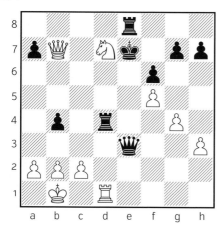

## (186)

▷ V. Kunin
► D. Van Dooren
Dutch league, 2016.11.05

1. +-

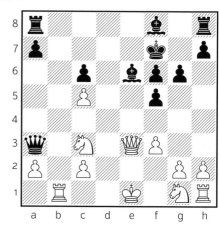

## (187)

▷ M. Matlakov
► F. Klein
European Club Cup, 2016.11.06

1. +-

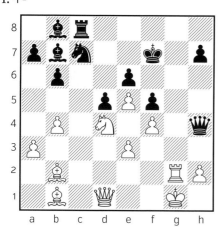

## (188)

▷ C. Landenbergue
► K. Sasikiran
European Club Cup, 2016.11.06

1... -+

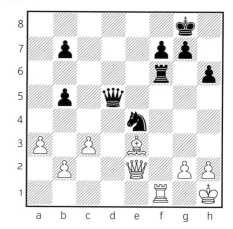

## (189)

▷ K. Landa
► V. Dragnev
Bad Wiessee, 2016.11.06

1. +-

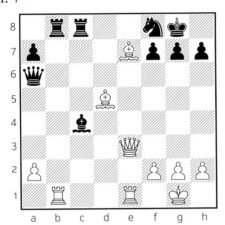

## (190)

▷ R. Rieger
► D. Dvirnyy
European Club Cup, 2016.11.07

1... -+

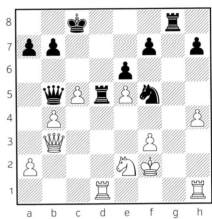

## (191)

▷ A. Greenfeld
► A. Naiditsch
European Club Cup, 2016.11.07

1. +-

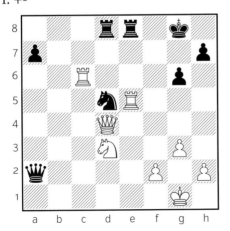

## (192)

▷ T. Radjabov
► A. Indjic
European Club Cup, 2016.11.08

1. +-

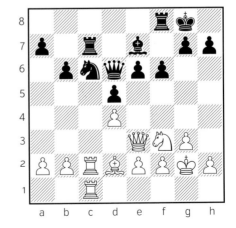

## (193)

▷ **D. Fridman**
▶ **J. Plenca**
Serbian Open, 2016.11.09

1. +-

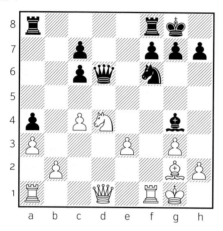

## (194)

▷ **Van de J. Griendt**
▶ **M. Bosiocic**
European Club Cup, 2016.11.10

1... -+

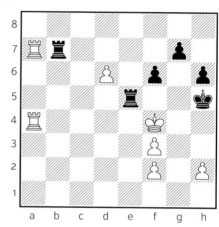

## (195)

▷ **S. Atalik**
▶ **N. Sulava**
Suleymanpasa GM, 2016.11.10

1... -+

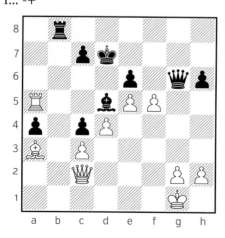

## (196)

▷ **V. Mikhalevski**
▶ **R. Faizrakhmanov**
European Club Cup, 2016.11.12

1... -+

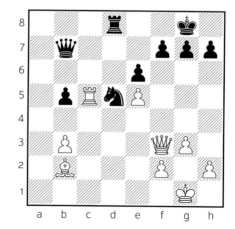

## (197)

▷ C. Lupulescu
► G. Papp
European Club Cup, 2016.11.12

1... -+

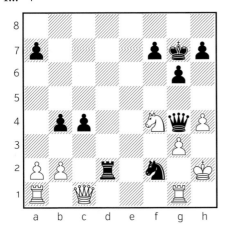

## (198)

▷ I. Ivanisevic
► G. Izsak
Hungarian league, 2016.11.13

1. +-

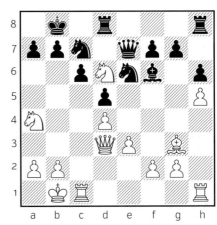

## (199)

▷ V. Topalov
► H. Nakamura
Champions Showdown Blitz, 2016.11.14

1... -+

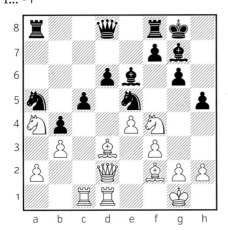

## (200)

▷ V. Anand
► V. Topalov
Champions Showdown Blitz, 2016.11.14

1. +-

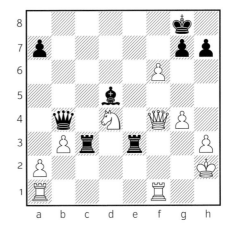

## (201)

▷ **M. Rodshtein**
► **M. Adams**
German league, 2016.11.19

1... -+

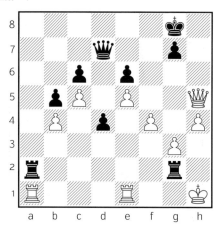

## (202)

▷ **D. Javakhadze**
► **S. Sevian**
Dallas, 2016.11.19

1... -+

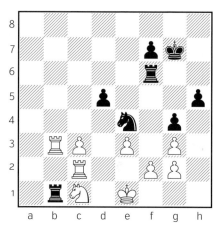

## (203)

▷ **S. Vidit**
► **K. Abhishek**
Indian Championship, 2016.11.21

1. +-

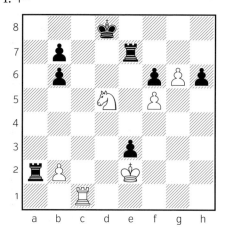

## (204)

▷ **V. Iordachescu**
► **L. Vajda**
Romanian league, 2016.11.21

1... -+

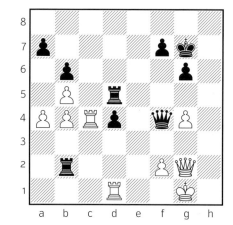

## (205)

▷ **A. Arribas Lopez**
► **V. Panchanatham**
Dallas Open, 2016.11.21

1. +-

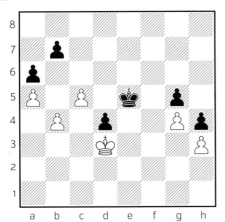

## (206)

▷ **L. Van Wely**
► **R. Kevlishili**
Dutch league, 2016.11.26

1. +-

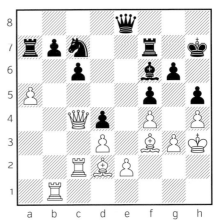

## (207)

▷ **S. Bromberger**
► **A. Muzychuk**
R. Munichpid, 2016.11.26

1... -+

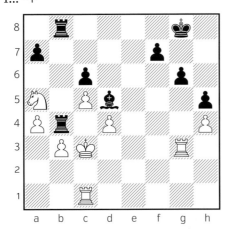

## (208)

▷ **P. Acs**
► **C. Horvath**
Hungarian league, 2016.11.27

1. +-

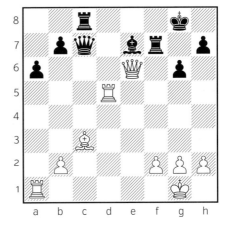

## (209)

▷ **V. Kramnik**
► **Hou Yifan**
Kings Blitz match, 2016.11.30

1. +-

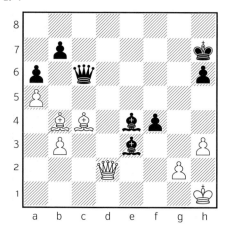

## (210)

▷ **B. Adhiban**
► **S. Vidit**
Indian Championship, 2016.11.30

1. +-

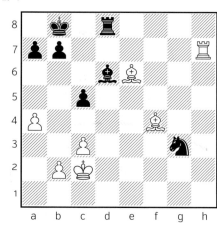

## (211)

▷ **Ni Hua**
► **Wang Chen**
Chinese league, 2016.12.02

1. +/-

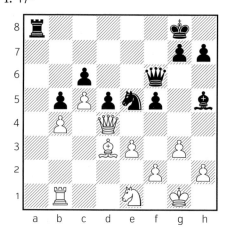

## (212)

▷ **E. Alekseev**
► **P. Smirnov**
Russian Rapid Cup, 2016.12.02

1. +-

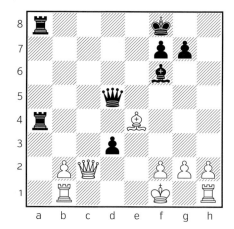

## (213)

▷ C. Schramm
► J. Smeets
German league, 2016.12.03

1... -+

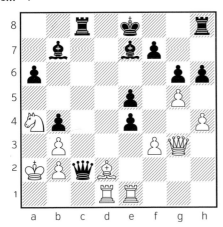

## (214)

▷ K. Landa
► M. Fedorovsky
German league, 2016.12.03

1. +-

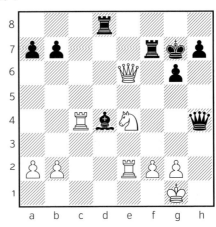

## (215)

▷ A. Timofeev
► P. Smirnov
Russian Cup, 2016.12.05

1... -+

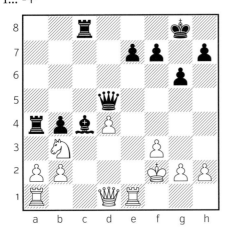

## (216)

▷ M. Roiz
► N. Birnboim
Israelian Championship, 2016.12.05

1. +-

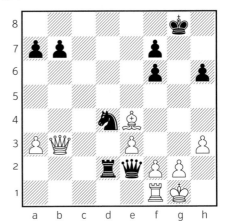

# (217)

 **Wen Yang**
► **Z. Zhang**
Hainan Open, 2016.12.11

1. +-

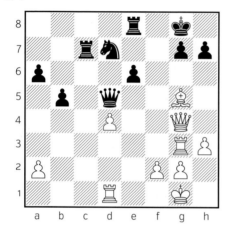

# – SOLUTIONS –

## (1)

▷ E. Sveshnikov
► N. Vitiugov
Keres memorial rapid, 08.01.2016

19...♘xb4 20.axb4 ♕xb4+ 21.♔f1 ♖xc5–+

## (2)

▷ Y. Krupenski
► M. Matlakov
Keres memorial rapid, 08.01.2016

34...♗xf2+! 35.♔f1 [35.♔xf2 ♖d2++; 35.♕xf2 ♖d1+ 36.♔g2 ♖d2–+] 35...♗b6–+

## (3)

▷ B. Gelfand
► I. Zhuk
Keres memorial rapid, 08.01.2016

11.♘g5! ♗xg5 [11...♗xg2 12.♕xh7#] 12.♗xb7+-

## (4)

▷ V. Sveshnikov
► N. Vitiugov
Keres memorial rapid, 10.01.2016

32...♕h1+! 33.♘xh1 ♖xh1# 0–1

## (5)

▷ K. Miton
► T. Kantans
Keres memorial rapid, 10.01.2016

33.♕xh7+! 1–0 [33.♕xh7+ ♔xh7 34.♖h3+ ♕h6 35.♖hxh6#]

## (6)

▷ D. Lintchevski
► E. Sutovsky
Keres memorial rapid, 10.01.2016

39...♖xd1! 40.♖xd1 ♔c2 0–1

## (7)

▷ M. Noble
► Ma Qun
New Zealand rapid, 11.01.2016

27...♖xg2! 0–1 [27...♖xg2 28.♖xg2 ♕h3 29.♕e2 ♕h1+–+]

## (8)

▷ A. Czebe
► I. Popov
Delhi Open, 12.01.2016

21...gxf4! 0–1 [21...gxf4 22.gxf5 f3+–+]

## (9)

▷ B. Adhiban
► N. Abasov
Wijk aan Zee B, 16.01.2016

20.♖ge1!! ♕h4 [20...♖xd2 21.♖e8#; 20...♖xe1 21.♕xf2+-] 21.♕xe2+-

## (10)

▷ K. Raghunandan
► V. Bernardskiy
Chennai Open, 19.01.2016

31...♘g3+! 32.hxg3 ♕xg3–+

## (11)

▷ S. Sevian
► B. Bok
Wijk aan Zee B, 23.01.2016

48...♖xc3+! 49.bxc3 ♕a3+ 50.♔c4
♕xc3+ 51.♔b5 ♕e5+ 52.♔xb4
♕xe7+ 53.♕xe7+ ♔xe7 54.♔c4=

## (12)

▷ B. Adhiban
► A. Dreev
Wijk aan Zee B, 23.01.2016

21.♖xd7! ♕xd7 22.♗b5 ♕xb5
23.♕xb5+ ♔f8 [23...♔e7 24.♕e5+
♔f8 25.♕d5 ♖c8 26.g3+- h6 (26...♗b2
27.♘g5+-; 26...f6 27.♘d4+-) 27.♘e5+-]
24.♕b3 1-0 [24.♕b3 ♗d6 (24...♗e7
25.♘e5+-) 25.♘g5+-]

## (13)

▷ E. Nakar
► D. Jakovenko
Gibraltar Open, 27.01.2016

30...♖xd3! 0-1 [30...♖xd3 31.cxd3
♖a2+ 32.♔f1 (32.♔e3 ♗c5+) 32...
♕a1#]

## (14)

▷ G. Jones
► P. Carlsson
Gibraltar Open, 27.01.2016

39.♕h8+! 1-0 [39.♕h8+ ♗xh8
40.♖xh8#]

## (15)

▷ M. Esserman
► E. Iturrizaga
Gibraltar Open, 27.01.2016

22...♘e3! 0-1 [22...♘e3 23.fxe3
♕xg3+ 24.♔h1 ♖f5-+]

## (16)

▷ F. Perez Ponsa
► R. Wojtaszek
Gibraltar Open, 01.02.2016

68...♔h7!! 0-1 [68...♖xg6=; 68...
fxg6=; 68...♔h7 69.♖xf6 (69.♖h6+
♖xh6-+) 69...♗d8 70.♔g5 ♔g7-+]

## (17)

▷ R. Padmini
► M. Al Sayed
Gibraltar Open, 01.02.2016

34.♖xf7+! ♖xf7 35.♕h6+ 1-0 [35.
♕h6+ ♔g8 36.♕g7#]

## (18)

▷ P. Harikrishna
► S. Vidit
Gibraltar Open, 02.02.2016

33.♕g5! 1-0 [33.♕g5 ♖xc2+ 34.♔g3
♕b6 35.f6+-]

## (19)

▷ R. Edouard
► V. Gunina
Gibraltar Open, 02.02.2016

21.♗xh7+! ♔f8 [21...♔xh7 22.♕h5+
♔g8 23.♖h3+-] 22.f4+-

## (20)

▷ A. Donchenko
► M. Esserman
Gibraltar Open, 03.02.2016

**24.♗xf7! ♖f8** [24...♔xf7 25.♕h7+
♔f8 26.♕xc7+-] **25.♗e6** [25.♗h5+-]
**25...♕d6 26.♖e3+-**

## (21)

▷ A. Schenk
► M. Bartel
German league, 06.02.2016

**48...♘g4+!** 0-1 [48...♘g4+ 49.♔f1
(49.♔h1 ♖h2#; 49.♔f3 ♖f2#) 49...
♘h2+ 50.♔e1 ♘f3+-+]

## (22)

▷ B. Gelfand
► A. Morozevich
Zurich, 13.02.2016

**45.c5! ♕e7** [45...bxc5 46.♗c4++-
] **46.♗c4+ ♔e8 47.♕xc6+ ♕d7
48.♕a8+ ♔e7 49.♕e4+ ♔d8
50.cxb6+-**

## (23)

▷ L. Aronian
► A. Shirov
Zurich blitz, 15.02.2016

**17.♘d5! ♕xe2** [17...♖xd5 18.cxd5
♕xe2 19.♖xe2 ♘xd5 20.♗xd5 ♗xd5
21.♖c1+-] **18.♘xe7+ ♔f8 19.♖xe2
♗xc4** [19...♔xe7 20.♗xc5+ ♔e8
21.♗xa7+-] **20.♖c2 ♗d3 21.♖xc5
♔xe7 22.♖xe5++-**

## (24)

▷ V. Anand
► H. Nakamura
Zurich blitz, 15.02.2016

**26.♗xh7+! ♔xh7 27.♕h6+ ♔g8
28.♖g1 ♕xg1+ 29.♔xg1+-**

## (25)

▷ A. Gupta
► C. Sochacki
Cappelle la Grande, 16.02.2016

**23.♘xh6+!** 1-0 [23.♘xh6+ gxh6
24.♕xh6 f6 (24...♘f5 25.♕h8#)
25.♕h7#]

## (26)

▷ C. Bauer
► V. Burmakin
Cappelle la Grande, 16.02.2016

**43.♕e8!** 1-0 [43.♕e8 hxg5 44.♕g8+
♔h6 (44...♔f6 45.♕f7#) 45.♕h8#]

## (27)

▷ S. Khademalsharieh
► V. Gunina
Tehran WGP, 18.02.2016

**62.♕xh5+! ♔e4** [62...♗xh5 63.♖f8+
♔e4 64.♖xf2+-] **63.♕g4++-**

## (28)

▷ N. Batsiashvili
► V. Gunina
Tehran WGP, 19.02.2016

**38...♗c5! 39.♕xc5 ♖e2** 0-1

## [29]

▷ M. Rodshtein
► M. Tazbir
German league, 20.02.2016

**26.♖e7+! ♔f8** [26...♗xe7 27.♕xe7#]
**27.♖f7+** 1–0

## [30]

▷ H. Koneru
► A. Stefanova
Tehran WGP, 23.02.2016

**25.♗xf7+! ♔xf7 26.♖xd7++-**

## [31]

▷ Wang Hao
► L. Dominguez
IMSA blitz, 28.02.2016

**21...♖xc3! 22.♖xd8 ♖xb3! 23.axb3**
[23.♖b8 ♖xb2+–+] **23...♔xd8–+**

## [32]

▷ P. Harikrishna
► D. Navara
IMSA blitz, 29.02.2016

**28.♕xa5!+-**   **♕c8**   [28...♕xa5
29.♖b8++–] **29.♕xc3** 1–0 [29.♕xc3
♕xc3 30.♖b8++-]

## [33]

▷ Wang Hao
► E. Tomashevsky
IMSA blitz, 01.03.2016

**67...d2+!** [67...♖xc5 68.d7+-] **68.♔xd2**
**♖xc5=**

## [34]

▷ R. Mamedov
► Wang Hao
IMSA blitz, 01.03.2016

**21...b5! 22.axb5** [22.♘a3 ♗xa3 (22...
bxa4) 23.♗xa3 b4 24.♗b2 ♗xf1∓]
**22...cxb5 23.♘a3 ♗xa3! 24.♗xa3 b4**
**25.♗b2 ♗xf1–+**

## [35]

▷ V. Ivanchuk
► G. Sargissian
IMSA blitz, 01.03.2016

**24.♘xd6! cxd6 25.♕xf7+-**

## [36]

▷ L. Dominguez
► S. Mamedyarov
IMSA blitz, 01.03.2016

**19.♖xe6!**   1–0   [19.♖xe6   fxe6
20.♕xe6+ ♔h7 21.♖xd8+-]

## [37]

▷ D. Navara
► S. Mamedyarov
IMSA rapid, 03.03.2016

**32.♖xf7+!** 1–0 [32.♖xf7+ ♔xf7
33.♕xd8+-]

## [38]

▷ L. Dominguez
► L. Fressinet
IMSA rapid, 03.03.2016

**24.♗xh6! ♗f6** [24...♗xh6 25.♖h4+-]
**25.♖f4+-**

## (39)

▷ C. Aravindh
► A. Motylev
Aeroflot Open, 09.03.2016

33...♘xf2!! 34.♖xd6 [34.♖xf2 ♖d1+
35.♖f1 ♖g2+ 36.♔h1 ♖xf1+–+] 34...
♘xh3+ 35.♔h1 ♘f2+ 36.♔g1 ♖xd6
37.♗xd6 ♘e4–+ 38.♗c7 ♖g2+
39.♔h1 ♘f2+ 0–1

## (40)

▷ A. Moiseenko
► B. Socko
German league, 13.03.2016

51...♖g1+! 52.♔xg1 ♕g3+ 53.♔h1
[53.♔f1 ♕f2#] 53...♕f3+ 54.♔g1 [54.
♔h2 ♗g3+ 55.♔h3 ♗f2+ 56.♔h2
♕g3+ 57.♔h1 ♕g1#] 54...♗f2+
55.♔h2 ♕g3+ 0–1

## (41)

▷ G. Popilski
► R. Li
Dallas, 15.03.2016

42...♖xe4! 0–1 [42...♖xe4 43.♕xe4
♕xf2+ 44.♔h1 ♕xc5–+]

## (42)

▷ H. Gretarsson
► J. Lind
Reykjavik Open, 15.03.2016

20.♘e6! fxe6 21.♗xa7+–

## (43)

▷ M. Sadler
► S. Chow
4NCL, 19.03.2016

59.g4! [59.♔d2? ♖g7 60.♔d3 ♔xg3=]
59...♖e7 [59...♔xe3 60.♖e8++–; 59...
fxg4 60.♖f8+ ♔xe3 61.♖e8++–; 59...
♔xg4 60.♖g8++–] 60.♔d2+–

## (44)

▷ N. Pert
► R. Williamson
4NCL, 19.03.2016

45.♖xg7! ♕xg7 [45...♔xg7 46.♕xh6+
♔g8 (46...♔f7 47.♕g6#) 47.♖g6+ ♔f7
48.♕h7+ ♔e8 49.♖e6++–] 46.♖xh6+
1–0 [46.♖xh6+ ♔g8 47.♕xd8++–]

## (45)

▷ Ni Hua
► M. Wecker
Grenke Open, 24.03.2016

36.♗xf7+! ♕xf7 [36...♔xf7
37.♕h5++–] 37.♗xh4+–

## (46)

▷ H. Melkumyan
► B. Atzmon Simon
Doeberl Cup, 24.03.2016

18.f5! ♕xg3 19.fxg6 ♕d6 20.♘xf7+–

## (47)

▷ J. Ikeda
► S. Ganguly
Doeberl Cup, 25.03.2016

36...♕xf2! 37.♗g2 [37.♖xf2 b1♕+
38.♖f1 ♖xh2+! 39.♔xh2 ♕xe4–+]
37...♖c1–+ 0–1

## (48)

▷ **T. Beerdsen**
► **Li Chao**
Grenke Open, 25.03.2016

37...♖xb2+! 38.♖xb2 [38.♔xb2 ♕xe2+–+] 38...♕xd1+–+

## (49)

▷ **S. Vidit**
► **I. Saeed**
Asian Nations Cup, 31.03.2016

30.♖xf7+! ♔xf7 31.♗xe6+ ♖xe6 32.♕xc7++-

## (50)

▷ **D. Milanovic**
► **K. Georgiev**
Karpos Open, 04.04.2016

39...♖c2! 0–1 [39...♖c2 40.♘xc2 ♕xf2+ 41.♔h1 ♕g1#]

## (51)

▷ **T. Nedev**
► **R. Markus**
Karpos Open, 05.04.2016

30...♖e3! 31.♖f3 [31.♕xe3 ♕xg2#] 31...♕xc3 32.♖xe3 ♕xd4–+

## (52)

▷ **L. Miron**
► **M. Parligras**
Romanian Champ., 05.04.2016

31...♗e3! 32.♗d6 ♕g4+! 33.♔f1 ♕f3! 34.♖a2 ♕h1+ 35.♔e2 ♕b1!–+

## (53)

▷ **E. Hossein**
► **M. Mosadeghpour**
Asian Nations Cup, 05.04.2016

72...♕a7! 73.♕xb3+ ♔c7 74.♕g3+ ♔b7 75.♕d6 [75.♕b3+ ♔a8–+] 75...a1♕+–+

## (54)

▷ **M. Santos Ruiz**
► **T. Gareev**
Colin Crouch Masters, 06.04.2016

34...♖xe6! 35.♖ce3 [35.♖xe6 ♖d1+–+] 35...♖xe3 36.fxe3 ♖g4+–+

## (55)

▷ **A. Bezgodov**
► **I. Lysyj**
Sergievskiy Memorial Rapid, 11.04.2016

18.♘xh7! ♘xh7 19.♕h6! 1–0

## (56)

▷ **H. Nakamura**
► **S. Shankland**
US Championship, 18.04.2016

26.♘xe6! ♗xg1 27.♖xg1 ♔h8 [27...♕xe6 28.♗xd5+-] 28.♕xd5+-

## (57)

▷ **A. Giri**
► **P. Eljanov**
Norway blitz, 18.04.2016

36.♖xh7+! 1–0

## (58)

▷ S. Zhigalko
► M. Petrosyan
Gaprindashvili Cup, 28.04.2016

26.♖g3+! ♔h7 27.♕h5! ♕xd1+
28.♕xd1 ♗xh6 29.exf6+-

## (59)

▷ D. Dubov
► V. Yandemirov
Russian league, 03.05.2016

34.♕xh7+! 1-0 [34.♕xh7+ ♔xh7
35.♘xf6+ ♔g7 36.♘xd7+-]

## (60)

▷ A. Korobov
► V. Yandemirov
Russian league, 06.05.2016

35.♖xf7! ♗xc2 [35...♖xf7 36.♗xg6+-]
36.♖xf8+ ♗xf8 37.♖xc2+-

## (61)

▷ M. Samusenko
► I. Popov
Russian league, 08.05.2016

31...♖d1! [31...♗xe4! 32.♖xe4 ♖d1!
33.♕xd1 ♕xf2+ 34.♔h1 ♕xg3-+]
32.♕xd1 ♕xf2+ 33.♔h1 ♗xe4+!
34.♖xe4 ♕xg3-+ 0-1

## (62)

▷ C. Lupulescu
► M. Godena
European Championship, 13.05.2016

32.♘d7+! ♖xd7 33.♕xf8+ ♔a7
34.♕f4+-

## (63)

▷ K. Kulaots
► A. Moiseenko
European Championship, 13.05.2016

30.♖xf8+! ♔xf8 31.♗h6+ ♖g7
[31...♔g8 32.♕c8++-] 32.♕f6+ ♔e8
33.♕xg7 1-0

## (64)

▷ S. Zhigalko
► A. Boruchovsky
European Championship, 14.05.2016

16.♖xd5! ♗d7 [16...exd5 17.♘xd5
♕d8 18.♗xc6+ bxc6 19.♕xc6+ ♗d7
20.♘f6+ ♔e7 21.♖d6#] 17.♖d3+-

## (65)

▷ F. Vallejo Pons
► M. Palac
European Championship, 14.05.2016

24.d6! ♗xd6 [24...♕xd6 25.♖xh8
♖xh8 26.♗xb5+-] 25.♖xf6 ♕e7
26.♕e4! ♕xf6 27.♕c6+ ♔b8 28.♗e4
1-0

## (66)

▷ M. Ragger
► S. Ter Sahakyan
European Championship, 17.05.2016

29...♖e8+! 30.♔d3 ♖xe2! 31.♔xe2
♘f4+ 32.♔f3 ♘xd5-+

## (67)

▷ B. Jobava
► E. Inarkiev
European Championship, 17.05.2016

**18...♘f2+! 19.♔g1** [19.♖xf2?? ♖xe1+ 20.♖f1 ♖xf1+ 21.♗xf1 ♕xd5+–+] **19... ♘h3+!** 1/2[19...♘h3+ 20.♔h1 ♘f2+=]

## (68)

▷ A. Ipatov
► H. Stefansson
European Championship, 17.05.2016

**34.♘xb6!** 1–0

## (69)

▷ D. Nisipeanu
► Z. Kozul
European Championship, 19.05.2016

**28.♖xf7+!!** ♕xf7 [28...♔xf7 29.♕h7+ ♔f8 30.♖g8#] **29.♕xd6+!** ♖e7 [29... ♘e7 30.♕h6++–; 29...♕e7 30.♕h6+ ♔f7 31.♕g7#] **30.♕xb8+** ♕e8 **31.♕d6** 1–0

## (70)

▷ R. Hovhannisyan
► J. Stocek
European Championship, 19.05.2016

**23.♖xe6!!** ♗d7 [23...fxe6 24.♖xe6 ♖xe6 25.♗xe6+ ♔f8 26.♗xc8+–] **24.♖xe8+ ♖xe8 25.♖xe8+ ♗xe8 26.♕c8+–**

## (71)

▷ S. Movsesian
► A. Shomoev
Kurnosov memorial, 27.05.2016

**25.♖xe7!** ♖xe7 **26.♘f6+** 1–0 [26. ♘f6+ ♔g7 27.♘xd7 ♖xd7 28.♗xc6+–]

## (72)

▷ S. Sethuraman
► D. Sengupta
Asian Continental, 30.05.2016

**24.♗d7!** ♖xd7 [24...♘xd7 25.♖xe7+–] **25.♖xd7 ♗c8** [25...♘xd7 26.♖xe8++–] **26.♖d6+–**

## (73)

▷ H. Stevic
► O. Letreguilly
French league, 01.06.2016

**27.♗c6+!** 1–0 [27.♗c6+ ♔xc6 (27... ♖xc6 28.♖a7++–) 28.♖c3++–]

## (74)

▷ K. Oliva
► I. Morovic Fernandez
American Continental, 01.06.2016

**33...♖e2+! 34.♕xe2 ♘d4+ 35.♔d2 ♘xe2 36.♔xe2 ♖d7–+**

## (75)

▷ A. Moskalenko
► A. Aleksandrov
Nezhmetdinov memorial,
02.06.2016

**14.♗xh7+!** ♔xh7 **15.♕h4+** ♔g8 **16.♘g5** ♖d8 **17.♕h7+** ♔f8 **18.♕h8+** ♔e7 **19.♕xg7** ♖f8 **20.♘e4→** [20.0-0-0+–; 20.♗h4+–]

## (76)

▷ R. Ponomariov
► N. Short
Neoclassical Masters rapid,
03.06.2016

24.♖xg6+! hxg6 25.♕xg6+ ♔h8
26.♗h3! ♕h7 [26...♕e7 27.♗g5+-]
27.♕f6+ ♔g8 28.♗e6+ ♖xe6
29.♕f8# 1–0

## (77)

▷ I. Ortiz Suarez
► S. Barrientos
American Continental, 03.06.2016

37...♖h1+! 0–1 [37...♖h1+ 38.♔xh1
♕xh3+ 39.♖h2 ♕f1#]

## (78)

▷ S. Mareco
► D. Flores
American Continental tiebreak,
05.06.2016

37...♗c4! 0–1 [37...♗c4 38.♗xc4
♕xg2#]

## (79)

▷ V. Kramnik
► M. Carlsen
Grand tour, Paris blitz, 11.06.2016

55...♖c3! 0–1 [55...♖c3 56.♗xg5
♖xf3+ 57.♔g2 ♔xe4–+]

## (80)

▷ A. Giri
► L. Fressinet
Grand tour, Paris blitz, 12.06.2016

18.♗xf5+! ♕xf5 19.♕xe8! 1–0

## (81)

▷ M. Carlsen
► F. Caruana
Grand tour, Leuven rapid, 17.06.2016

45...♖xg2+! 46.♔xg2 ♘d4 47.♔g1
♘xf3+! 48.♔f2 ♘d4–+ [48...
♘h4!–+]

## (82)

▷ P. Svidler
► M. Kazhgaleyev
Eurasian Blitz Championship,
18.06.2016

17.♗xg5! ♕e8 [17...hxg5 18.♗h7+ ♔h8
19.♗g6+ ♔g8 20.♕h7#] 18.♕xe8
♖fxe8 19.♗xe7 ♖xe7 20.♗d5+-

## (83)

▷ V. Onischuk
► S. Karjakin
Eurasian blitz, 18.06.2016

30...♗xf2+! 31.♔h1 [31.♔xf2 ♕c2–+]
31...♕xf3 32.gxf3 ♗xe1–+

## (84)

▷ Le Quang Liem
► D. Makhnyov
Eurasian Blitz Championship,
18.06.2016

25.♖xc5 ♖xc5 26.♘xe6 ♖d5 [26...
fxe6 27.♗xc5+-] 27.♘xf8 ♖xd1+
28.♕xd1+-

## (85)

▷ I. Gaponenko
► A. Dreev
Eurasian Blitz Championship,
18.06.2016

24...♕xe1+! 25.♗xe1 ♖xe1+ 26.♗f1
♘e3!–+ 0–1

## (86)

▷ O. Dzyuban
► I. Saric
Eurasian Blitz Chapionship,
18.06.2016

36...♖xf3! 37.♕g1 [37.gxf3 ♕h2#;
37.♖xf3 ♕xa1+–+] 37...♖a3?∞ [37...
♗e3! 38.gxf3 (38.♕h2 ♖xf1+ 39.♖xf1
a1♕ –+) 38...♗xg1 39.♔xg1 ♔f8–+]

## (87)

▷ O. Dzyuban
► I. Saric
Eurasian Blitz Championship,
18.06.2016

43...♖xh3+! 0–1 [43...♖xh3+ 44.gxh3
♕xh3+ 45.♖h2 ♕f3+ 46.♖g2 ♕h5+
47.♖h2 ♕xd1+–+ 48.♔g2 ♕g1+
49.♔h3 ♕e3+ 50.♔g2 ♕f2+ 51.♔h3
♕f3+ 52.♔h4 g5+ 53.♔xg5 ♕f4+
54.♔h5 ♕xh2+–+]

## (88)

▷ I. Nepomniachtchi
► A. Aleksandrov
Eurasian blitz, 19.06.2016

22.♕xb8! 1–0 [22.♕xb8 ♖xb8 (22...
♕xe4 23.♕xf8+ ♔xf8 24.♖xe4+-)
23.♖e8+ ♖xe8 24.♖xe8#]

## (89)

▷ W. So
► V. Kramnik
Grand tour, Leuven blitz, 20.06.2016

41...♖xd4+! 0–1 [41...♖xd4+ 42.exd4
♖xa3–+]

## (90)

▷ V. Sviridov
► V. Fedoseev
Russian Higher league, 22.06.2016

29...♖xa3+! 30.bxa3 ♕xa3+ 31.♔b1
♕a2# 0–1

## (91)

▷ A. Riazantsev
► A. Predke
Russian Higher league, 22.06.2016

34.♖xf7! ♔xf7 35.♕f4+! ♔e7 [35...
♔g6 36.♕g4+=] 36.♕c7+ ♔f6
37.♕f4+=

## (92)

▷ M. Carlsen
► T. Petrosian
Internet blitz, 23.06.2016

24.e5! fxe5 [24...♘xe5 25.♘xe5 fxe5
26.♕xg5++-] 25.♘xe6+ ♕xe6
26.♘xg5+- 1–0

## (93)

▷ M. Vavulin
► G. Oparin
Russian Higher league, 25.06.2016

33...♖c1+! 34.♖xc1 ♗d3+ 35.♔a1
♕xc1+ 36.♔a2 ♕b1+ 37.♔b3 ♕c2+

0–1 [37...♕c2+ 38.♔a2 ♗c4+ 39.♔a1 ♕c1#]

## (94)

▷ I. Bocharov
► D. Kurberinov
Russian Higher league, 25.06.2016

17.♖xg7+! ♔xg7 18.♗g5 [18.♗h6+ ♔h8 19.♗g5+-] 18...♘d7 [18...♘d6 19.♕h6++-] 19.♖g1 ♔h8 20.♗xd8 ♖axd8 21.♘xc4+-

## (95)

▷ M. Oganian
► I. Khairullin
Russian Higher league, 27.06.2016

29...♖xf2! 30.♔xf2 ♕xh2+ 31.♔f1 ♖e2!–+ 32.♖d8+ ♔h7 33.♕b1+ g6 34.♕xg6+ ♔xg6 0–1

## (96)

▷ K. Alekseenko
► S. Lobanov
Russian Higher league, 27.06.2016

26.♖xe6+! 1–0 [26.♖xe6+ fxe6 27.♕xg6+ ♕f7 28.d7+!+-]

## (97)

▷ A. Sarana
► S. Volkov
Russian Higher league, 28.06.2016

32...♖f7!! [32...♕c4? 33.♕f6+] 33.♖xh4 [33.♕xf7 ♕xh1+–+] 33... ♖xf3 34.♖xb4 ♘d7–+

## (98)

▷ L. Lenic
► J. Skoberne
Vidmar memorial, 28.06.2016

16.c5! ♕c7 [16...dxc5 17.e5+-] 17.♗g3+- [17.cxd6+-]

## (99)

▷ D. Kokarev
► K. Alekseenko
Russian Higher league, 28.06.2016

37.♗xe5! ♖xe5 38.♕h3 ♖f8 39.♕h8+ ♔f7 40.♕h5+! 1–0 [40.♕h5+ ♔g8 41.♕g6++-]

## (100)

▷ N. Capone
► G. Jones
Porticcio Open, 30.06.2016

32...♘xg3! 33.♖d1 [33.♔xg3 ♖e1!–+] 33...♖e1 34.♖xd2 ♖f8–+

## (101)

▷ D. Khismatullin
► A. Gabrielian
Russian Higher league, 01.07.2016

25.♗xf7+! ♔xf7 26.♕a2+ ♘e6 27.♖xd8+-

## (102)

▷ D. Dubov
► V. Sviridov
Russian Higher league, 01.07.2016

28.♘xb5! cxb5 [28...♕xb5 29.♖b3+-] 29.♖c3! 1–0 [29.♖c3 ♕d5 30.♕xb5+ ♕xb5 31.♖xb5+ ♔a8 32.♖a3#]

# (103)

▷ A. Shimanov
► Y. Zherebukh
Annual World Open, 04.07.2016

**20.♗f6!** 1–0 [20.♗f6 ♗xf6 (20...♘xf6
21.♕g5#) 21.♘xf6+ ♘xf6 22.♕g5#]

# (104)

▷ G. Arnaudov
► I. Saric
Greek league, 05.07.2016

**26...♕xf3!** 0–1 [26...♕xf3 27.♕xf3
♗xg5+ 28.♖xg5 ♖xf3–+]

# (105)

▷ B. Veltkamp
► E. Alekseev
Amsterdam Open, 09.07.2016

**9...b5! 10.cxb5 c4–+**

# (106)

▷ E. Najer
► R. Buhmann
Dortmund, 09.07.2016

**27.♘xe6! ♗xe6 28.♖h8+ ♔xg7
29.♖xa8+-**

# (107)

▷ P. Harikrishna
► Ding Liren
Danzhou, 10.07.2016

**40.e4! ♗xe4 41.♕xd3!** 1–0

# (108)

▷ Bu Xiangzhi
► V. Ivanchuk
Danzhou, 10.07.2016

**55.♖g5+!** [55.h8♕? ♕e1+–+] **55...♔e4
56.♖e5+!** 1–0 [56.♖e5+ ♕xe5 (56...
♔d4 57.h8♕+-) 57.fxe5 ♖f8 58.♘f6+
♔xe5 59.♘g8+-]

# (109)

▷ M. Bartel
► B. Lalith
Najdorf memorial, 10.07.2016

**44.♘f8+! ♗xf8** [44...♖xf8
45.♖xg7++-] **45.h8♕+-**

# (110)

▷ A. Areshchenko
► A. Fier
Najdorf memorial, 13.07.2016

**34.♖e7! ♘xe7 35.dxe7 ♖b8** [35...
♕xe7 36.♕xg6+ ♔h8 37.♕h6+ ♕h7
38.♗xf6++-] **36.exf8♕++-**

# (111)

▷ E. Najer
► M. Vachier Lagrave
Dortmund, 15.07.2016

**27...♘c5! 28.0-0** [28.♕xe5 ♘xd3+
29.♔e2 ♘xe5–+] **28...♘xd3 29.♕xd3
♗d7–+**

# (112)

▷ B. Savchenko
► P. Gelazonia
Aleksandria Cup, 16.07.2016

**34.♘e7+!** 1-0 [34.♘e7+ ♛xe7
35.♛xc8++-]

## (113)

▷ **A. Gupta**
► **A. Smirnov**
Najdorf memorial, 16.07.2016

**31.♘xf7!** ♖a6 [31...♔xf7 32.♖xd6+-;
31...♘xf7 32.♖xb7++-] **32.♖xa6**
**♗xa6 33.♘7e5!+-**

## (114)

▷ **M. Carlsen**
► **A. Giri**
Bilbao, 22.07.2016

**38.♘xf5!** ♛e6 [38...♛xf5 39.♛xd5+
♛f7 40.♛xa8++-] **39.♛g5 g6** [39...
♛xe5 40.♘h6++-] **40.♘h6+ ♔f8**
**41.♘g4+-**

## (115)

▷ **V. Ivanchuk**
► **S. Mamedyarov**
Turkish league, 30.07.2016

**46.♖xe4!** 1-0 [46.♖xe4 ♛xe4
47.♛g5+ ♔f8 48.♛g7#]

## (116)

▷ **Yu Lie**
► **Zhao Jun**
Chinese league, 31.07.2016

**28.dxc7!** ♛g4+ **29.♔h2** 1-0 [29.
♔h2 ♖xf6 (29...♖bc8 30.♖d8+-)
30.cxb8♛++-]

## (117)

▷ **N. Vitiugov**
► **A. Kovchan**
Biel Open, 31.07.2016

**30.♖xf7!** 1-0 [30.♖xf7 ♛xf7 (30...
♔xf7 31.♛xh7++-) 31.♖xg6+ ♔h8
32.♖g7+-]

## (118)

▷ **K. Sasikiran**
► **M. Al Sayed**
Biel Open, 02.08.2016

**25.e7!** ♛xe7 **26.♖fe1** 1-0 [26.♖fe1
♛c5 27.♛g6+ ♗g7 28.♗e5+-]

## (119)

▷ **A. Fier**
► **O. Romanishin**
Fano Open, 04.08.2016

**20.♖d6!** ♘f4 [20...♛c7 21.♖xd5+-]
**21.exf4 ♛c7 22.♖d5!+-**

## (120)

▷ **M. Vachier Lagrave**
► **V. Anand**
Sinquefield Cup, 06.08.2016

**31...e3!** **32.♗xe3** [32.♗g3 e2-+] **32...**
**♗xd5 33.♗xa7+** [33.♖xd5 ♛xe3+-+]
**33...♔xa7-+**

## (121)

▷ **J. Xiong**
► **C. Menezes**
World Juniors, 09.08.2016

**36.♘xe6!** ♖xe6 **37.♖xe6+ ♘xe6**
**38.♖xe6+! ♔xe6 39.♗f5+ ♔d6**
**40.♗xc8+-**

## (122)

▷ V. Topalov
► Ding Liren
Sinquefield Cup, 09.08.2016

**65.♖c7!** [65.♖c5+? ♔h4=; 65.g3? ♗g2+ 66.♘xg2 ♖xg2=] **65...g6** [65... ♗xg2+ 66.♘xg2 ♖xg2 67.♖xg7++-] **66.g3!** 1–0

## (123)

▷ S. Gagare
► B. Ivekovic
World Juniors, 09.08.2016

**30...♕c1+! 31.♖xc1 ♖xc1+ 32.♗f1 ♗h3–+ 33.♕a8+ ♔g7** 0–1

## (124)

▷ K. Sasikiran
► I. Sukandar
Vlissingen Open, 10.08.2016

**21.♘xe6! ♖xe6 22.♗xd5 ♗f7 23.♕xb2+-**

## (125)

▷ C. Menezes
► Q. Yuan
World Juniors, 14.08.2016

**30.♘g6+! hxg6 31.♕h4+** 1–0

## (126)

▷ E. Rozentalis
► L. Johansson
Manhem GM, 18.08.2016

**26.♖1f3! ♕xd4** [26...♕e1 27.♖xd7 ♖xf3 (27...♕xb1 28.♖ff7+-) 28.♕xf3 ♕xb1 29.♕f7+ ♔h8 30.♕xg7#]

**27.♖xd7 ♖xf3 28.♕xf3 ♕xe5+ 29.♕g3+-**.

## (127)

▷ J. DegraeveM
► V. Veys
French Championship, 21.08.2016

**30.♖xe5! ♕d3** [30...♕xe5 31.♕xg6+-; 30...♖xg2 31.♖xf5+-] **31.♖e3!** 1–0

## (128)

▷ M. Swayams
► B. Adhiban
Abu Dhabi Open, 22.08.2016

**100...♘g2! 101.♗g6 d2!** 0–1 [101...d2 102.♔e2 ♘xf4+ 103.♔xd2 ♘xg6–+]

## (129)

▷ V. Petkov
► E. Cordova
Spanish league, 22.08.2016

**33.♖xb7! ♘xb7 34.♗xa6 ♖b8 35.♗xb7! ♖xb7 36.♘xd5!** 1–0

## (130)

▷ H. Melkumyan
► T. Ravi
Abu Dhabi Open, 22.08.2016

**22.♘xh6!** [22.♗xh6? gxh6 23.♖g3 ♘f6!] **22...♘f6** [22...gxh6 23.♖g3+- ♘f6 24.♗e5 ♘bd7 25.♕g8#] **23.♘xf7+ ♔g8 24.♕g6+-**

## (131)

▷ Y. Fang
► Y. Weii
Chinese Rapid Champ., 25.08.2016

**62...♖c1+!** 0–1 [62...♖c1+ 63.♖xc1 ♕xb6–+]

## (132)

▷ S. Sevian
► R. Panjwani
US Masters, 26.08.2016

**41.♗f7+!** 1–0 [41.♗f7+ ♔xf7 42.♘xb6++-]

## (133)

▷ S. Vidit
► L. Aguilar
Olympiad, 02.09.2016

**22.♗xh6!** ♗f6 [22...♗xh6 23.♖h3+-; 22...♗xd4 23.♕xd4 ♔xh6 24.♖h3++-] **23.♗g5+-**

## (134)

▷ V. Topalov
► S. Nadir
Olympiad, 02.09.2016

**30.♘xe6!** [30.♘xc6!? ♖xd2 31.♘e7+ ♔f7 32.♘xg6 ♖d1+ 33.♔g2 ♖d2+ 34.♔h3±] **30...♖e8** [30...♖xd2 31.♕f8#; 30...♕xe6 31.♖xd8++-] **31.♘c5+-** 1–0

## (135)

▷ D. Navara
► P. Eljanov
Olympiad, 02.09.2016

**34...♕xe6! 35.dxe6 ♘e2+** 0–1

## (136)

▷ L. Fressinet
► W. Lorenzana
Olympiad, 02.09.2016

**29.♖xg7+! ♕xg7 30.♕xe6+** 1–0 [30. ♕xe6+ ♕f7 31.♕xc8++-]

## (137)

▷ Y. Atabayev
► V. Kramnik
Olympiad, 03.09.2016

**39...♘a4!!** 0–1 [39...♘a4 40.bxa4 ♖xe3–+ (*40...b3–+*) ]

## (138)

▷ B. Adhiban
► S. Minero Pineda
Olympiad, 03.09.2016

**47.♗f6!!** ♖xf6 **48.♖a6+** 1–0 [48. ♖a6+ ♔e7 49.♖xf6 ♔xf6 50.f8♕++-]

## (139)

▷ D. Svetushkin
► I. Nepomniachtchi
Olympiad, 04.09.2016

**42...♕e1! 43.♘f3** [43.♕xc8 ♕xf2+ 44.♔h1 ♕g1#] **43...♗xh3+! 44.♔xh3 ♕xf1+ 45.♔h2 ♗xf2–+**

## (140)

▷ D. Jakovenko
► I. Popov
Moscow blitz, 04.09.2016

**24.♗xc5! ♕xc5 25.♖d8+! ♔h7** [25... ♖xd8 26.♕xc5+-] **26.♖xc8** 1–0 [26. ♖xc8 ♕xc8 27.♕xb6+-]

### (141)

▷ J. Cubas
► K. Stupak
Olympiad, 04.09.2016

**28…♕xh2+!** 0–1 [28…♕xh2+ 29.♔xh2 ♖h4+ 30.♖h3 ♖xh3#]

### (142)

▷ F. Caruana
► F. Peralta
Olympiad, 04.09.2016

**40.♖xf5!** [40.♗b4+ ♔xe6 41.♖e5+ ♔d7] **40…a1♕ 41.♖xa1 ♖xa1 42.♗b4+!** 1–0 [42.♗b4+ ♔xe6 43.♖e5+ ♔f6 44.♖xe2+-]

### (143)

▷ J. Pineda
► F. Berkes
Olympiad, 05.09.2016

**33…♖c2+! 34.♖e2 g6! 35.♕f3 ♕d1!** 0–1

### (144)

▷ L'E. Ami
► D. Howell
Olympiad, 05.09.2016

**37.♘h6+!** [37.♕xd5!? ♖xd5 (37…♗xd5 38.♖cd3!+-) 38.♘e7+! ♖xe7 39.♖c8+ ♖e8 40.♖xe8+ ♗xe8 41.♖xd5+-] **37… gxh6** [37…♔f8 38.♕b4++-] **38.♕g4+ ♔f8 39.♖xd5+-**

### (145)

▷ B. Bok
► G. Jones
Olympiad, 05.09.2016

**29.♘xe7! ♖xe7 30.♕xd6 ♘c6 31.♕xc5+-**

### (146)

▷ A. Brkic
► B. Kalezic
Olympiad, 06.09.2016

**39.♕g7+! ♖gxg7 40.fxg7+ ♔g8** [40… ♖xg7 41.♖e8++-] **41.♖e8+** 1–0

### (147)

▷ M. Kolago
► Y. Vovk
Polish league, 07.09.2016

**33…♖c2+! 34.♔g1** [34.♕xc2 ♘e3+ 35.♔g1 ♘xc2-+] **34…♗f2+! 35.♔h1 ♘e3!-+ 36.♗g2 ♖c1+ 37.♔h2 ♗g1+ 38.♔h1 ♗f2+ 39.♔h2 ♖g1** 0–1

### (148)

▷ T. Nedev
► F. Amonatov
Olympiad, 08.09.2016

**24…♘c3+! 25.bxc3** [25.♕xc3 ♕xd6-+] **25…♕xa5 26.♕d5** [26.c4 ♕a4-+] **26…♖c5-+** 0–1

### (149)

▷ M. Kazhgaleyev
► A. Neiksans
Olympiad, 08.09.2016

**44…d4!! 45.exd4** [45.♔e4 d3! 46.♔xd3 ♖a3!-+] **45…♖a3! 46.♖xa3 b1♕-+**

## (150)

▷ E. Hansen
▶ A. Zhigalko
Olympiad, 08.09.2016

**28.e5!** ♔d7 [28...♗xe5 29.♘xe6+ ♖xe6 30.♕xb4+-] **29.exf6+-**

## (151)

▷ E. Hossain
▶ I. Ivanisevic
Olympiad, 09.09.2016

**40.♘e5+! dxe5 41.♖xa6+-**

## (152)

▷ A. Mijovic
▶ V. Cmilyte
Olympiad Women, 10.09.2016

**29...♗c3! 30.♕xc3 ♘xe4 31.♖xe4 ♕xe4–+**

## (153)

▷ S. Mareco
▶ J. Sadorra
Olympiad, 11.09.2016

**50...♘xf4!** 0–1 [50...♘xf4 51.♖xe6 ♘d3+ 52.♔f1 ♘xb4–+]

## (154)

▷ V. Laznicka
▶ L'E. Ami
Olympiad, 11.09.2016

**36.♗a6!!** 1–0 [36.♗a6 ♕xa6 (36... ♕c7 37.♗b5+-; 36...♕d7 37.♗b5+-; 36...♕a8 37.♗b5+-) 37.♕xc6+-]

## (155)

▷ P. Harikrishna
▶ S. Karjakin
Olympiad, 12.09.2016

**27.♘hf6+** ♔h8 [27...gxf6 28.♘xh6+ ♔h7 29.♘xf5+-] **28.♘xe8+-**

## (156)

▷ M. Carlsen
▶ E. Ghaem Maghami
Olympiad, 12.09.2016

**25.♖xf7+!** [25.♖f4? ♖gd8∞] **25... ♔xf7 26.♘d6++-**

## (157)

▷ E. Hansen
▶ S. Shankland
Olympiad, 13.09.2016

**42.♘c5!** 1–0 [42.♘c5 ♕xc5 43.♕e8+ ♔h7 44.♕g6+ ♔g8 45.♖e8++-]

## (158)

▷ E. Inarkiev
▶ Hou Yifan
Rapid match, 17.09.2016

**31...g4!** 32.♕c3 [32.♕xg4 ♗h5–+] **32...gxh3–+**

## (159)

▷ Hou Yifan
▶ E. Inarkiev
Rapid match, 17.09.2016

**27.♖xa7! ♕xa7 28.♖xd8+-**

## (160)

▷ B. Grachev
► E. Kretov
Moscow Rapid, 17.09.2016

**15.** ♗xh7+! ♔xh7 **16.** ♕h4+ 1–0 [16.
♕h4+ ♔g8 17.♘g5+-]

## (161)

▷ R. Rapport
► M. Antipov
Spanish league, 27.09.2016

**34.** ♖xg7! 1–0 [34.♖xg7 ♗xg7
35.♗xg7+ ♔g8 36.♕xd5 ♗xd5
37.♗e5+ ♔f8 38.♗xb8+-]

## (162)

▷ E. Romanov
► R. Hasangatin
Russian Rapid Championship,
02.10.2016

**19.** ♗xf7+! ♘xf7 **20.** ♘e6+-

## (163)

▷ A. Rakhamov
► P. Ponkratov
Russian Rapid Championship,
02.10.2016

**18.** ♕h5! 1–0 [18.♕h5 gxh5 19.♖g3+
♗g5 20.♖xg5#]

## (164)

▷ D. Dubov
► V. Zakhartsov
Russian Rapid Championship,
02.10.2016

**26.** ♗xg7! ♔xg7 **27.** ♕g5+ ♔f8
**28.** ♕h6+ ♔g8 **29.** ♕g5+ ♔f8

**30.** ♗xh3!+- ♕c6 [30...♖d1 31.♕h6+
♔g8 (31...♔e7 32.♕d6#) 32.♗f5!
♖xf1+ 33.♔xf1 ♕d1+ 34.♔f2 ♕d4+
35.♔g2 ♕xe5 36.♗h7+ ♔h8 37.♗g6+
♔g8 38.♕h7+ ♔f8 39.♕xf7#] **31.** ♕h5!
♕c7 **32.** ♕h8+ ♔e7 **33.** ♖xf7+ 1–0

## (165)

▷ S. Vidit
► B. Lalith
Isle of Man, 05.10.2016

**34.** ♗e5! f6 [34...♕xe5 35.♕xd8+-]
**35.** ♗xf6+-

## (166)

▷ A. Morozevich
► G. Kamsky
Russian Rapid league, 05.10.2016

**20.** ♗e5! ♖h7 [20...♖g8 21.♕f7+-]
**21.** ♕g6! e6 **22.** ♗xd6! ♗xd6
**23.** ♕g8++-

## (167)

▷ F. Caruana
► S. Movsesian
Isle of Man, 05.10.2016

**27.** ♖de1! ♕b5 [27...♖xd6 28.♖e8+
♖xe8 29.♖xe8#] **28.** ♕e5+-

## (168)

▷ A. Alexeev
► V. Bologan
Russian Rapid league, 05.10.2016

**13.** b5! ♗xg2 [13...♘xd5 14.bxc6+-;
13...♘d8 14.♗xe7+ ♕xe7 15.♗xh3+-]
**14.** bxc6 ♕h3 **15.** ♘xe7+ ♔h8 **16.** f3
♗xf1 **17.** ♕xf1+-

## (169)

▷ A. Karpov
► J. Timman
Basamro match, 08.10.2016

31...♘xb3! 32.axb3 ♖xa1 33.♖xa1
♖xc2 34.♖a7 ♘f6! 35.♖xb7 ♘xd5–+

## (170)

▷ P. Wallace
► A. Salem
Isle of Man, 09.10.2016

38...♖xd3! 39.cxd3 ♕a2+ 40.♔f2
♕xb1 41.♕xg6+ ♔d7–+

## (171)

▷ I. Cheparinov
► S. Bekker Jensen
Croatian league, 09.10.2016

9.♗xf6! ♗xf6 10.♘g5! ♗xg5
11.♗xb7 ♘d7 12.♗xa8 ♕xa8
13.♕xc4+-

## (172)

▷ I. Cheparinov
► Z. Kozul
Croatian league, 16.10.2016

35.♗d5+! ♔xd6 [35...♔xd5 36.d7+-]
36.♗xb3+-

## (173)

▷ M. Adams
► S. Kindermann
German league, 16.10.2016

18.♘xf7! ♔xf7 19.♕xe4±

## (174)

▷ D. Jakovenko
► A. Goganov
Russian Championship, 17.10.2016

58...c2! 59.♗e2 [59.♗xc2 ♗xa4–+;
59.♖xc2 ♖d7+! 60.♔e3 ♖xd1–+] 59...
♗xa4–+

## (175)

▷ V. Artemiev
► O. Biriukov
Chigorin memorial, 20.10.2016

32.♖xe5! ♗xb3 [32...fxe5 33.♖f8++-]
33.axb3 1–0

## (176)

▷ D. Navara
► K. Bulski
Slovakian league, 22.10.2016

33.♘xe6! ♖c6 [33...fxe6 34.♕xe6+
♗f7 35.♕xc8+-] 34.♘xf8! ♔xf8
35.♗d6+ ♔g8 36.♕e7 1–0

## (177)

▷ T. Gharamian
► D. Vocaturo
Corsican Circuit, 27.10.2016

19.♗xf7+!! ♔h8 [19...♖xf7
20.♕xa8++-; 19...♔xf7 20.♕d5+ ♔g6
21.♖g4+-] 20.♖d7+-

## (178)

▷ D. Bocharov
► E. Tomashevsky
Russian Championship, 27.10.2016

38...♖xg3! 39.hxg3 ♖f2+–+

## (179)

▷ A. Korobov
► Hou Yifan
Corsican Circuit, 28.10.2016

22.♗xe4! fxe4 23.♕xg5! ♖f6 24.♘d2+-

## (180)

▷ T. Nabaty
► B. Murtazin
Karadzica memorial, 30.10.2016

17.♗f6! 1–0 [17.♗f6 gxf6 18.♕h6+-]

## (181)

▷ Yu Yangyi
► Wang Yue
Chinese league, 31.10.2016

38.♖xh5+! ♔g7 [38...gxh5 39.♖h6+ ♔g7 40.♕g5+ ♔f8 41.♖h8#] 39.♕d4+- [39.♖xg6+! fxg6 40.♕d4+ ♔f7 41.♖h7+ ♔f8 42.♕g7#]

## (182)

▷ T. Nabaty
► J. Skoberne
Karadzica memorial, 01.11.2016

34.♖xg6+! 1–0 [34.♖xg6+ ♔xg6 35.♖g1+ ♔f6 (35...♔h5 36.♕h7#) 36.♕g7#]

## (183)

▷ D. Komarov
► A. Fier
Payakht Cup, 01.11.2016

24.♕xg7+! ♔xg7 25.gxf5+ ♔f6 26.fxe6+-

## (184)

▷ E. Torre
► B. Damljanovic
Suleymanpasa GM, 05.11.2016

45.♕d8+! ♔h7 46.♘xg5+! hxg5 47.♖e7+-

## (185)

▷ T. Luther
► S. Danailov
Suleymanpasa GM, 05.11.2016

32.♘e5+! ♔d6 [32...♔f8 33.♕f7#] 33.♘c4+! 1–0 [33.♘c4+ ♔c5 34.♘xe3+-]

## (186)

▷ V. Kunin
► D. Van Dooren
Dutch league, 05.11.2016

16.♖b7+ ♗e7 17.♖xe7+! 1–0 [17.♖xe7+ ♔xe7 18.♘d5+ cxd5 19.♕xa3+-]

## (187)

▷ M. Matlakov
► F. Klein
European Club Cup, 06.11.2016

27.♗xf5! exf5 28.♘xf5 ♕h3 29.♘d6++-

## (188)

▷ C. Landenbergue
► K. Sasikiran
European Club Cup, 06.11.2016

29...♕h5! 0–1 [29...♕h5 30.♕xh5 ♖xf1+ 31.♗g1 ♘f2#]

## (189)

▷ K. Landa
► V. Dragnev
Bad Wiessee, 06.11.2016

**28.♖xb8! ♖xb8 29.♕f4!** 1–0 [29.♕f4 ♗xd5 30.♕xb8+–]

## (190)

▷ R. Rieger
► D. Dvirnyy
European Club Cup, 07.11.2016

**23...♖g2+! 24.♔xg2 ♕xe2+ 25.♔h3 ♘e3!–+ 26.♖dg1 ♕xf3+** 0–1

## (191)

▷ A. Greenfeld
► A. Naiditsch
European Club Cup, 07.11.2016

**37.♖d6! ♖xd6 38.♖xe8+ ♔f7 39.♕h8+–**

## (192)

▷ T. Radjabov
► A. Indjic
European Club Cup, 08.11.2016

**20.♗b4!** 1–0 [20.♗b4 ♕xb4 (20... ♕d7 21.♗xe7+–) 21.♕xe6+ ♔h8 22.♖xc6+–]

## (193)

▷ D. Fridman
► J. Plenca
Serbian Open, 09.11.2016

**18.♖xf6! ♕xf6** [18...♗xd1 19.♖xd6 cxd6 20.♖xd1+–] **19.♕xg4+–**

## (194)

▷ Van de J. Griendt
► M. Bosiocic
European Club Cup, 10.11.2016

**34...♔h4!! 35.♖e4** [35.♖xb7 g5#] **35... g5+ 36.♔e3+ ♖xe4+ 37.fxe4 ♖xa7–+**

## (195)

▷ S. Atalik
► N. Sulava
Suleymanpasa GM, 10.11.2016

**32...♖b1+!** 0–1 [32...♖b1+ 33.♕xb1 (33.♔f2 ♕xg2+–+) 33...♕xg2#]

## (196)

▷ V. Mikhalevski
► R. Faizrakhmanov
European Club Cup, 12.11.2016

**28...♘f4!!** 0–1 [28...♘e3!!–+; 28...♘f4 29.♕xb7 (29.♕xf4 ♖d1#) 29...♖d1#]

## (197)

▷ C. Lupulescu
► G. Papp
European Club Cup, 12.11.2016

**35...♕h3+!!** 0–1 [35...♕h3+ 36.♘xh3 ♘g4+ 37.♔h1 ♖h2#]

## (198)

▷ I. Ivanisevic
► G. Izsak
Hungarian league, 13.11.2016

**22.♖xc6! bxc6 23.♕b3+ ♘b5** [23... ♔a8 24.♕b7#] **24.♘f5+!+–** 1–0

## (199)

▷ V. Topalov
► H. Nakamura
Champions Showdown Blitz,
14.11.2016

20...♗xb3! 21.axb3 ♞xb3 22.♕c2 ♞xc1 23.♖xc1 ♗h6!–+ 0–1

## (200)

▷ V. Anand
► V. Topalov
Champions Showdown Blitz,
14.11.2016

30.f7+! 1–0 [30.f7+ ♔f8 31.♞e6+! ♗xe6 32.♕xb4++–]

## (201)

▷ M. Rodshtein
► M. Adams
German league, 19.11.2016

45...♖h2+! 46.♔g1 ♖h1+! 0–1 [46...♖h1+ 47.♔xh1 ♕d5+ 48.♔g1 ♕g2#]

## (202)

▷ D. Javakhadze
► S. Sevian
Dallas, 19.11.2016

58...♖xf2! 59.♖xb1 [59.♖xf2 ♖xc1+ 60.♔e2 ♖c2+–+] 59...♖xc2–+

## (203)

▷ S. Vidit
► K. Abhishek
Indian Championship, 21.11.2016

33.♖c8+! ♔xc8 34.♞xe7+ ♔d7 35.g7 ♖xb2+ 36.♔xe3 ♖g2 37.♞g6!+– 1–0

## (204)

▷ V. Iordachescu
► L. Vajda
Romanian league, 21.11.2016

53...♖xf2! 0–1 [53...♖xf2 54.♕xd5 (54.♕xf2 ♕xg4+ 55.♕g2 ♕xd1+–+) 54...♕g3+ 55.♔h1 ♖h2#]

## (205)

▷ A. Arribas Lopez
► V. Panchanatham
Dallas Open, 21.11.2016

44.b5! axb5 [44...♔d5 45.c6! bxc6 46.bxa6+–] 45.c6! ♔d6 [45...bxc6 46.a6+–] 46.cxb7 ♔c7 47.a6 b4 48.♔xd4+– 1–0

## (206)

▷ L. Van Wely
► R. Kevlishili
Dutch league, 26.11.2016

34.♖xb7! ♖xb7 35.♗xc6+– 1–0

## (207)

▷ S. Bromberger
► A. Muzychuk
Munich, Rapid, 26.11.2016

29...♖xb3+! 0–1 [29...♖xb3+ 30.♞xb3 ♖xb3+ 31.♔c2 ♖xg3–+]

## (208)

▷ P. Acs
► C. Horvath
Hungarian league, 27.11.2016

28.♖d7! ♕c5 29.♖xe7!+- 1-0 [29.
♖xe7 ♕xe7 (29...♕xf2+ 30.♔h1+-)
30.♕xc8++-]

## (209)

▷ V. Kramnik
► Hou Yifan
Kings Blitz match, 30.11.2016

40.♕d8! ♗xg2+ 41.♔h2 ♕g6
42.♕e7++-

## (210)

▷ B. Adhiban
► S. Vidit
Indian Championship, 30.11.2016

28.♖h8! ♖xh8 29.♗xd6+ ♔a8
30.♗xg3+-

## (211)

▷ Ni Hua
► Wang Chen
Chinese league, 02.12.2016

27.♗xb5! ♖a2 [27...cxb5 28.♕xd5+
♔f8 29.♕xa8++-] 28.♗f1+-

## (212)

▷ E. Alekseev
► P. Smirnov
Russian Rapid Cup, 02.12.2016

25.♕xa4!+- 1-0

## (213)

▷ C. Schramm
► J. Smeets
German league, 03.12.2016

24...♕xb3+! 0-1 [24...♕xb3+
25.♔xb3 ♗d5#]

## (214)

▷ K. Landa
► M. Fedorovsky
German league, 03.12.2016

24.♖xd4! 1-0 [24.♖xd4 ♖xd4
25.♕e5+ ♔g8 26.♕xd4+-]

## (215)

▷ A. Timofeev
► P. Smirnov
Russian Cup, 05.12.2016

23...♖xa2! 0-1 [23...♖xa2 24.♖xa2
♗xb3 25.♖a5 ♖c2+! 26.♕xc2 (26.
♔g1 ♕xa5-+) 26...♕xd4+ 27.♔g3
♗xc2-+]

## (216)

▷ M. Roiz
► N. Birnboim
Israelian Championship, 05.12.2016

29.♗h7+! ♔xh7 [29...♔g7 30.exd4+-]
30.♕xf7+ ♔h8 31.exd4+-

## (217)

▷ Wen Yang
► Z. Zhang
Hainan Open, 11.12.2016

41.♗d8!+- 1-0 [41.♗f4? ♘f6!]

# (1)

▷ **V. Mikhalevski**
► **V. Sveshnikov**
Keres memorial rapid, 2016.01.08

1. +-

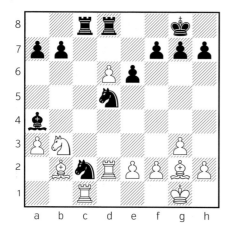

# (2)

▷ **Y. Krupenski**
► **B. Gelfand**
Keres memorial rapid, 2016.01.08

1. +-

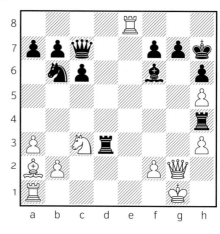

# (3)

▷ **K. Georgiev**
► **E. Romanov**
Keres memorial rapid, 2016.01.08

1. +-

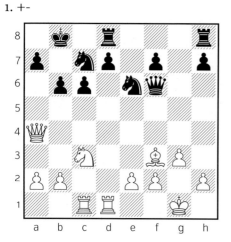

# (4)

▷ **F. Berkes**
► **D. Lintchevski**
Keres memorial rapid, 2016.01.09

1. +-

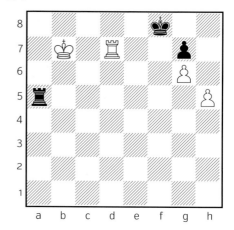

## (5)

▷ **I. Popov**
► **A. Demchenko**
Delhi Open, 2016.01.12

1. +/−

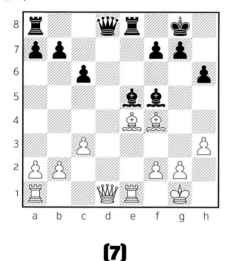

## (6)

▷ **Ma Qun**
► **R. Dive**
New Zealand rapid, 2016.01.12

1. +−

## (7)

▷ **N. Torosyan**
► **R. Hovhanissyan**
Armenian Championship, 2016.01.15

1... −+

## (8)

▷ **K. Grigoryan**
► **L. Babujian**
Armenian Championship, 2016.01.15

1... −+

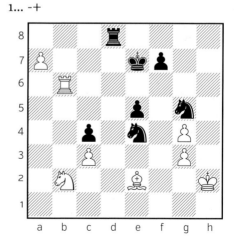

# (9)

▷ **D. Nisipeanu**
► **N. Batsiashvili**
Wijk aan Zee B, 2016.01.16

1. +-

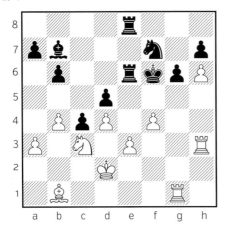

# (10)

▷ **T. Banusz**
► **K. Motuz**
Slovakian league, 2016.01.17

1. +-

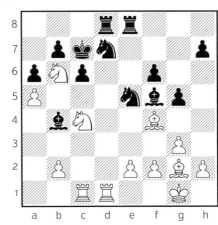

# (11)

▷ **D. Shailesh**
► **Nguyen Huynh Minh Huy**
Chennai Open, 2016.01.19

1. +-

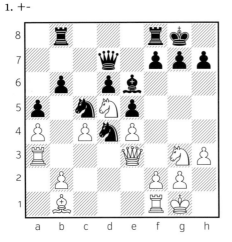

# (12)

▷ **B. Bok**
► **E. Safarli**
Wijk aan Zee B, 2016.01.19

1... -+

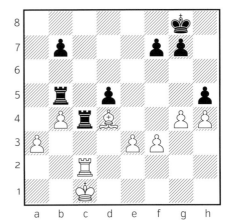

# (13)

▷ L. Van Wely
► M. Carlsen
Wijk aan Zee A, 2016.01.21

1... -+

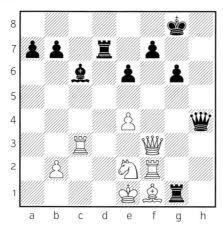

# (14)

▷ B. Adhiban
► A. Dreev
Wijk aan Zee B, 2016.01.23

1. +-

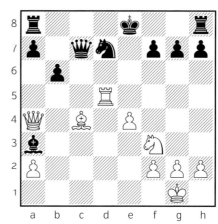

# (15)

▷ H. Nakamura
► R. Bellin
Gibraltar Open, 2016.01.26

1. +-

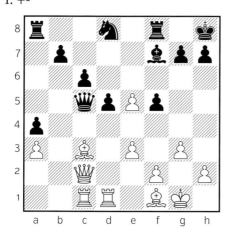

# (16)

▷ S. Mihajlov
► Ni Hua
Gibraltar Open, 2016.01.26

1... -+

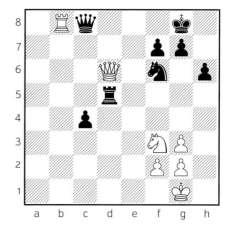

# (17)

▷ **M. Admiraal**
► **B. Bok**
Wijk aan Zee B, 2016.01.26

1... -+

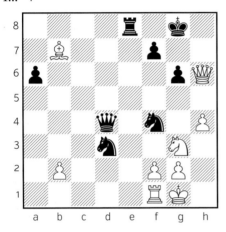

# (18)

▷ **E. Tomashevsky**
► **Ding Liren**
Wijk aan Zee A, 2016.01.29

1... -+

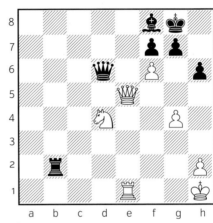

# (19)

▷ **P. Vishnu**
► **B. Kohlweyer**
Gibraltar Open, 2016.02.01

1. +-

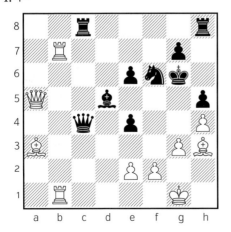

# (20)

▷ **L. Shytaj**
► **A. Donchenko**
Gibraltar Open, 2016.02.02

1. +-

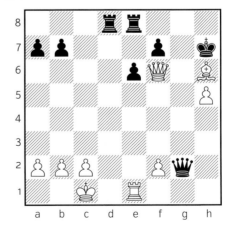

# (21)

▷ **L. Lenic**
▶ **R. Padmini**
Gibraltar Open, 2016.02.02

1. +-

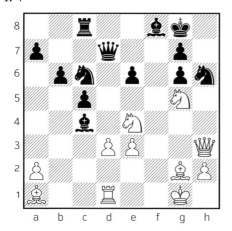

# (22)

▷ **Li Chao**
▶ **B. Uksini**
Graz Open, 2016.02.12

1. +-

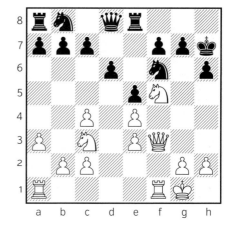

# (23)

▷ **G. Kamsky**
▶ **D'L. Costa**
Cappelle la Grande Open, 2016.02.13

1. +-

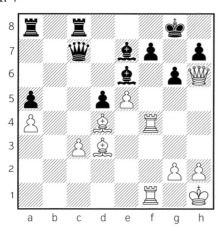

# (24)

▷ **V. Anand**
▶ **L. Aronian**
Zurich, 2016.02.13

1. +-

## (25)

▷ M. Daels
► E. Blomqvist
Cappelle la Grande, 2016.02.17

1... -+

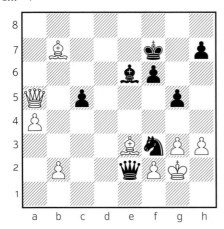

## (26)

▷ G. Kamsky
► M. Kazhgaleyev
Cappelle la Grande, 2016.02.18

1. +-

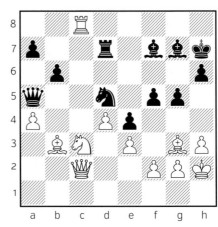

## (27)

▷ N. Zhukova
► N. Pogonina
Tehran WGP, 2016.02.22

1. +/-

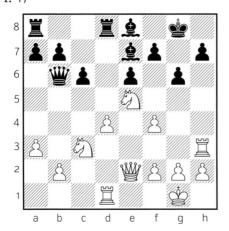

## (28)

▷ G. Kilgus
► B. Predojevic
Austrian league, 2016.02.25

1... -+

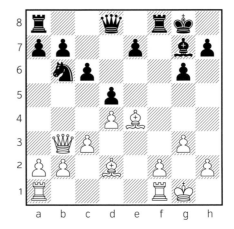

## (29)

▷ S. Movsesian
► Li Chao
IMSA rapid, 2016.02.26

1... -+

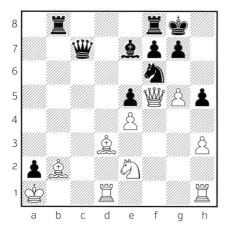

## (30)

▷ V. Ivanchuk
► R. Wojtaszek
IMSA blitz, 2016.03.01

1... =

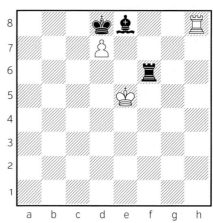

## (31)

▷ V. Ivanchuk
► Ding Liren
IMSA basque, 2016.03.02

1... -+

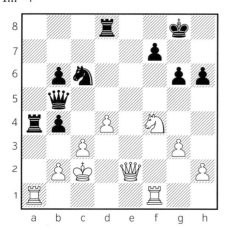

## (32)

▷ B. Lalith
► A. Salem
Aeroflot Open, 2016.03.08

1... -+

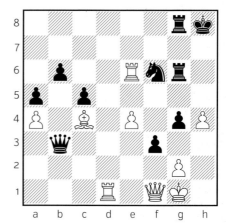

## (33)

▷ **D. Dubov**
► **A. Moiseenko**
Aeroflot Open, 2016.03.08

1. +-

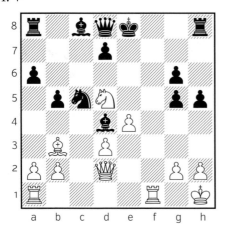

## (34)

▷ **M. Muzychuk**
► **Hou Yifan**
World Championship, 2016.03.09

1... -+

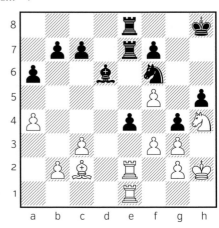

## (35)

▷ **P. Meister**
► **R. Edouard**
German league, 2016.03.12

1... -/+

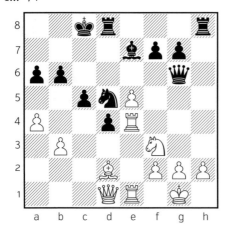

## (36)

▷ **S. Karjakin**
► **H. Nakamura**
Candidates, 2016.03.12

1. +-

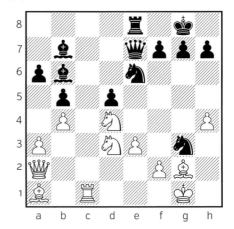

# (37)

▷ **K. Duda**
▶ **M. Rodshtein**
German league, 2016.03.13

1. +−

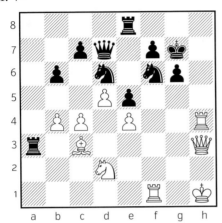

# (38)

▷ **S. Cicak**
▶ **N. Grandelius**
Swedish league, 2016.03.19

1... −+

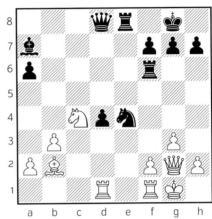

# (39)

▷ **P. Svidler**
▶ **H. Nakamura**
Candidates, 2016.03.23

1... =

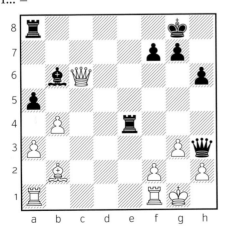

# (40)

▷ **R. Garcia Pantoja**
▶ **E. Cordova**
Mexican Open, 2016.03.24

1. +−

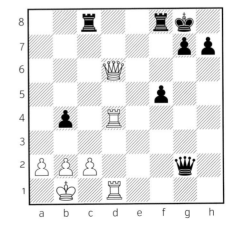

## (41)

▷ E. Cordova
► J. Flores Guerrero
Mexican Open, 2016.03.24

1. +-

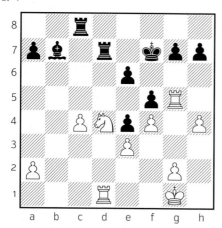

## (42)

▷ Li Chao
► V. Fedoseev
Grenke Open, 2016.03.28

1... -+

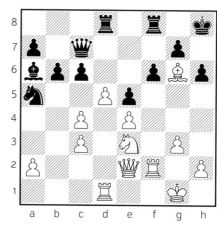

## (43)

▷ M. Klekowski
► R. Wojtaszek
Polish Championship, 2016.03.30

1... -/+

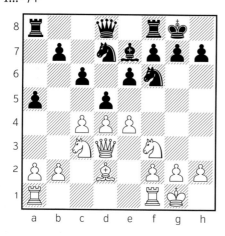

## (44)

▷ G. Popilski
► G. Kamsky
Calgary Open, 2016.03.31

1. +-

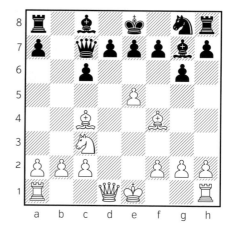

# (45)

▷ **N. Murshed**
► **R. Jumabayev**
Asian Nations Cup, 2016.04.02

1. +-

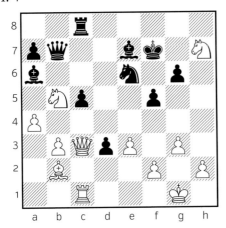

# (46)

▷ **D. Swiercz**
► **M. Kanarek**
Polish Championship, 2016.04.05

1. +-

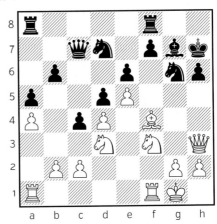

# (47)

▷ **D. Svetushkin**
► **D. Dvirnyy**
Karpos Open, 2016.04.05

1. +-

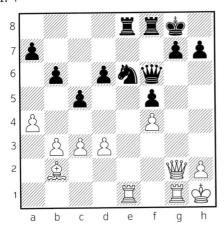

# (48)

▷ **V. Jianu**
► **A. Dolana**
Romanian Championship, 2016.04.05

1... -+

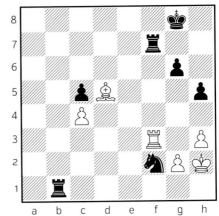

## (49)

▷ **I. Khairullin**
► **V. Antonio**
Bangkok Open, 2016.04.13

1. +−

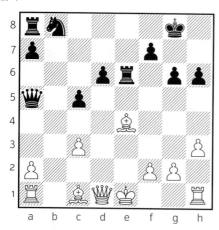

## (50)

▷ **F. Vallejo Pons**
► **Wynn Zaw Htun**
Bangkok Open, 2016.04.15

1. +−

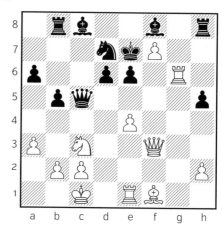

## (51)

▷ **B. Jobava**
► **C. Krishna**
Dubai Open, 2016.04.16

1. +−

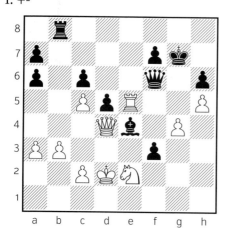

## (52)

▷ **M. Vachier Lagrave**
► **P. Eljanov**
Norway blitz, 2016.04.18

1. +−

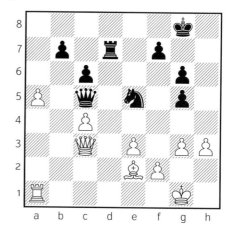

# (53)

▷ **L. Pantsulaia**
► **S. Sethuraman**
Dubai Open, 2016.04.18

1. +−

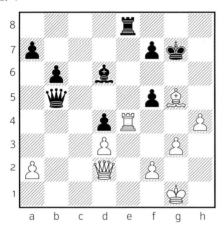

# (54)

▷ **Gao Rui**
► **Y. Xu**
Chinese Championship, 2016.04.19

1... −+

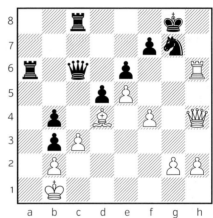

# (55)

▷ **N. Guliyev**
► **L. Riemersma**
Dutch league, 2016.04.23

1. +−

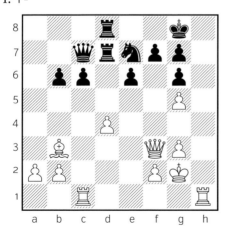

# (56)

▷ **H. Nakamura**
► **J. Xiong**
US Championship, 2016.04.24

1. +−

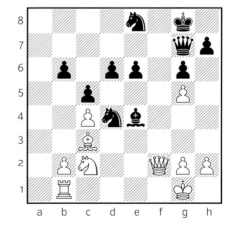

## (57)

▷ **A. Giri**
► **N. Grandelius**
Norway Chess, 2016.04.28

1. =

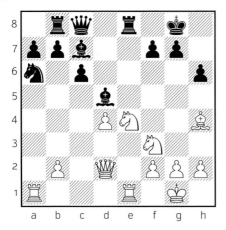

## (58)

▷ **W. So**
► **H. Nakamura**
Ultimate Chess Challenge, 2016.04.29

1...-+

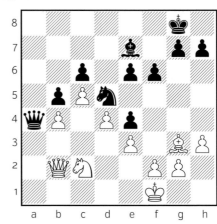

## (59)

▷ **G. Kasparov**
► **W. So**
Ultimate Chess Challenge, 2016.04.29

1... =

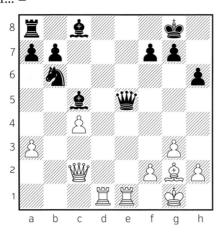

## (60)

▷ **S. Rublevsky**
► **D. Frolyanov**
Russian league, 2016.05.03

1. +-

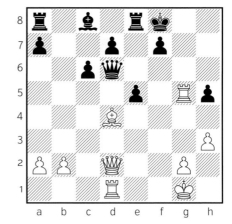

## (61)

▷ V. Artemiev
► E. Inarkiev
Russian league, 2016.05.08

1... -/+

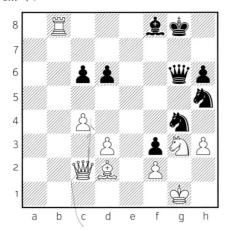

## (62)

▷ A. Predke
► V. Yandemirov
Russian league, 2016.05.09

1. +-

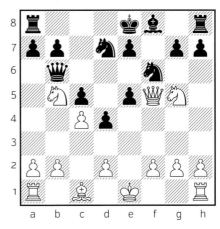

## (63)

▷ M. Vachier Lagrave
► F. Caruana
Internet blitz, 2016.05.10

1... -+

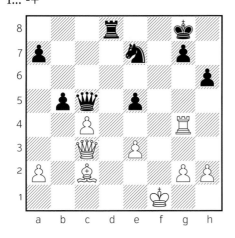

## (64)

▷ E. Inarkiev
► D. Svetushkin
European Championship, 2016.05.13

1. +-

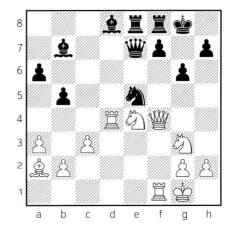

## (65)

▷ I. Cheparinov
► L. Pantsulaia
European Championship, 2016.05.16

1. +-

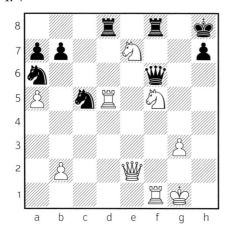

## (66)

▷ E. Blomqvist
► E. Romanov
European Championship, 2016.05.16

1... -+

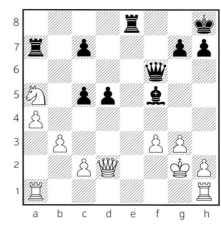

## (67)

▷ M. Gagunashvili
► D. Dubov
European Championship, 2016.05.19

1... -+

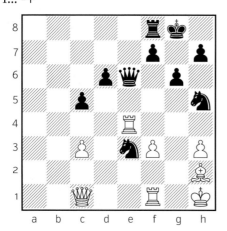

## (68)

▷ D. Navara
► A. Pashikian
European Championship, 2016.05.23

1. +-

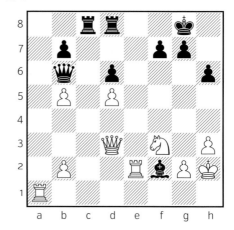

## (69)

▷ **A. Grischuk**
► **I. Kuznetsov**
Kurnosov memorial, 2016.05.26

1. +-

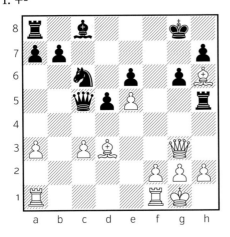

## (70)

▷ **A. Giri**
► **S. Karjakin**
Shamkir, 2016.05.27

1. +-

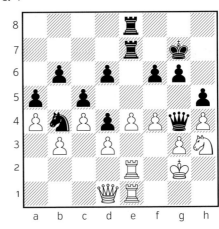

## (71)

▷ **A. Fedorov**
► **D. Ospennikov**
Nezhmetdinov Mem. Rapid, 2016.05.28

1. +-

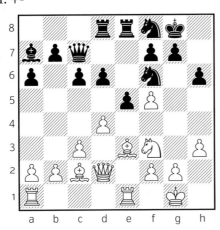

## (72)

▷ **A. Sumets**
► **A. Naiditsch**
French league, 2016.05.30

1... -+

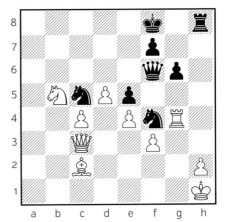

# (73)

▷ **S. Mamedyarov**
► **E. Safarli**
Shamkir, 2016.06.02

1. +/-

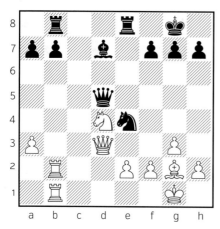

# (74)

▷ **A. Timofeev**
► **A. Sharafiev**
Nezhmetdinov memorial, 2016.06.04

1. +-

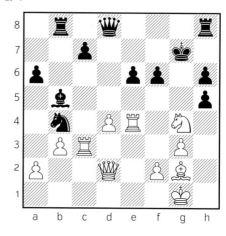

# (75)

▷ **F. Caruana**
► **M. Carlsen**
Grand tour, Paris rapid, 2016.06.09

1... -/+

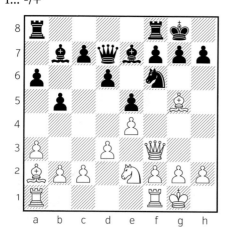

# (76)

▷ **V. Kramnik**
► **F. Caruana**
Grand tour, Paris rapid, 2016.06.10

1. +-

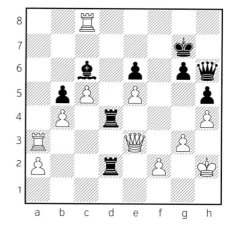

# (77)

▷ **A. Giri**
► **L. Fressinet**
Grand tour, Paris rapid, 2016.06.10

1. +−

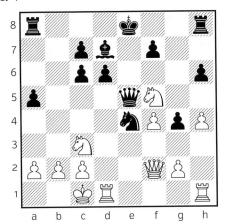

# (78)

▷ **L. Fressinet**
► **V. Kramnik**
Grand tour, Paris rapid, 2016.06.10

1... −+

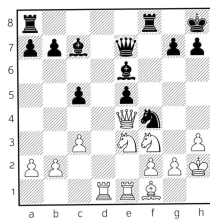

# (79)

▷ **F. Caruana**
► **M. Vachier Lagrave**
Grand tour, Paris rapid, 2016.06.10

1... −+

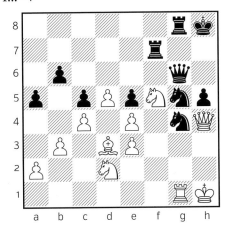

# (80)

▷ **W. So**
► **M. Carlsen**
Grand tour, Paris blitz, 2016.06.12

1... −+

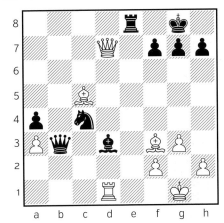

# (81)

▷ A. Giri
► M. Carlsen
Grand tour, Paris blitz, 2016.06.12

1. +-

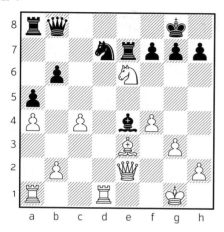

# (82)

▷ F. Caruana
► V. Anand
Grand tour, Leuven rapid, 2016.06.17

1. +-

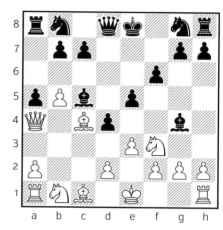

# (83)

▷ A. Stefanova
► G. Jones
Eurasian blitz, 2016.06.18

1... -+

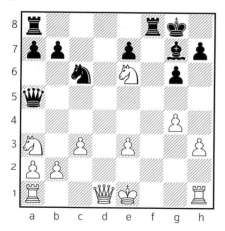

# (84)

▷ S. Movsesian
► J. Van Foreest
Teplice Open, 2016.06.18

1. +-

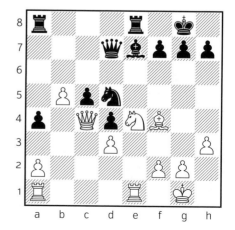

## (85)

▷ **S. Karjakin**
► **V. Onischuk**
Eurasian blitz, 2016.06.18

1. +−

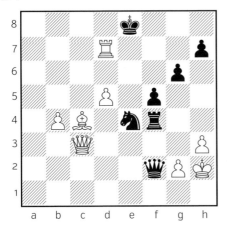

## (86)

▷ **A. Gabrielian**
► **A. Cherniaev**
Russian Higher league, 2016.06.27

1. +−

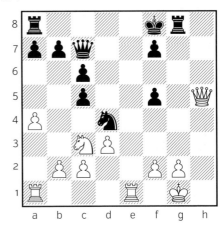

## (87)

▷ **V. Zvjagintsev**
► **A. Timofeev**
Russian Higher league, 2016.06.29

1. +/−

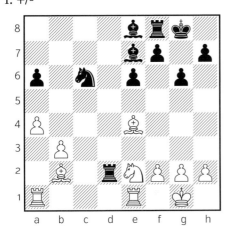

## (88)

▷ **R. Kurbedinov**
► **D. Rodin**
Russian Higher league, 2016.06.29

1... −+

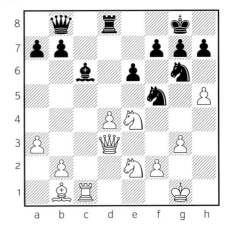

## (89)

▷ **S. Volkov**
► **A. Predke**
Russian Higher league, 2016.07.01

1. +-

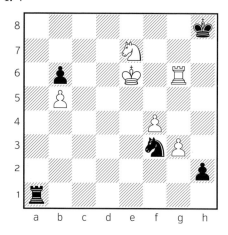

## (90)

▷ **A. Gorovets**
► **V. Bologan**
World Open, 2016.07.02

1... -+

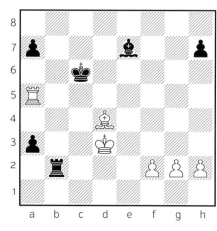

## (91)

▷ **S. Pozo Vera**
► **S. Sevian**
Annual World Open, 2016.07.04

1... -+

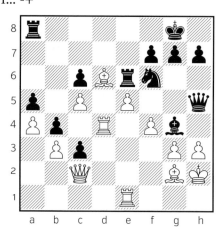

## (92)

▷ **T. Sanikidze**
► **A. Mikaelyan**
Batumi, 2016.07.09

1... -+

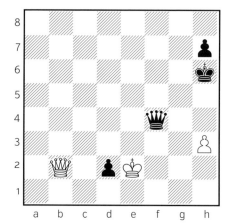

# (93)

▷ **G. Jones**
► **A. Puranik**
Najdorf memorial, 2016.07.09

1... -+

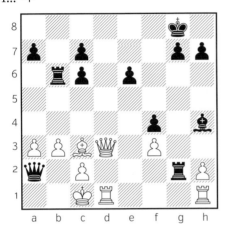

# (94)

▷ **P. Leko**
► **I. Nepomniachtchi**
Danzhou, 2016.07.11

1... -+

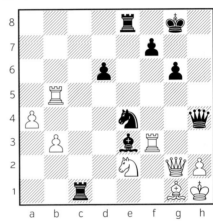

# (95)

▷ **B. Savchenko**
► **Z. Bayramov**
Alexandria Cup, 2016.07.13

1... -+

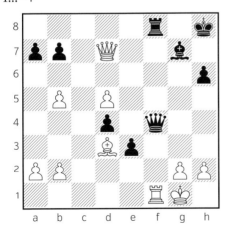

# (96)

▷ **B. Gelfand**
► **E. Inarkiev**
Magas match, 2016.07.14

1. +-

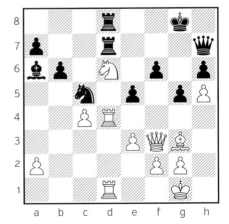

## (97)

▷ **Z. Efimenko**
► **M. Krasenkow**
Najdorf memorial, 2016.07.14

1. +-

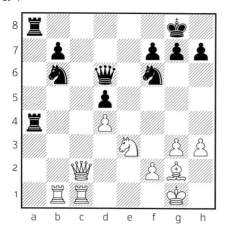

## (98)

▷ **B. Savchenko**
► **V. Danielyan**
Aleksandria Cup, 2016.07.15

1. +-

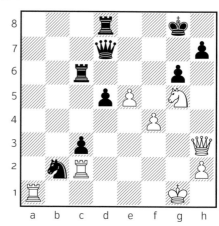

## (99)

▷ **P. Leko**
► **V. Ivanchuk**
Danzhou, 2016.07.16

1... -+

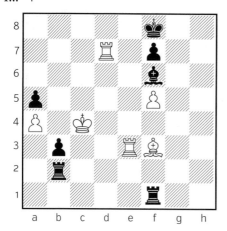

## (100)

▷ **K. Piorun**
► **B. Dubansky**
Pardubice rapid, 2016.07.20

1. +-

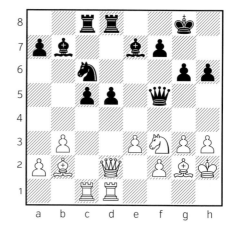

# (101)

▷ **B. Gelfand**
► **E. Inarkiev**
Magas match, 2016.07.20

1. +-

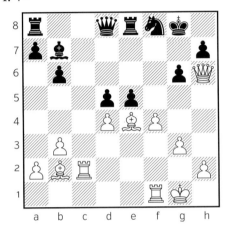

# (102)

▷ **V. Onischuk**
► **J. Duda**
Lake Sevan, 2016.07.24

1. +-

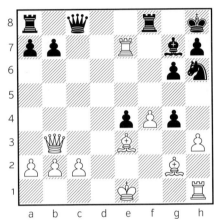

# (103)

▷ **S. Ganguly**
► **V. Jansa**
Pardubice, 2016.07.24

1. +-

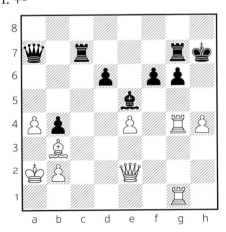

# (104)

▷ **M. Matlakov**
► **V. Bologan**
Poikovsky, 2016.07.25

1. +-

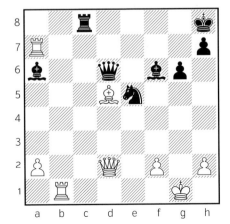

## (105)

▷ G. Gaehwiler
► R. Jumabayev
Biel Open, 2016.07.26

1. +-

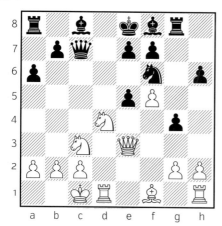

## (106)

▷ A. Dreev
► T. Ringoir
Xtracon Open, 2016.07.26

1. +-

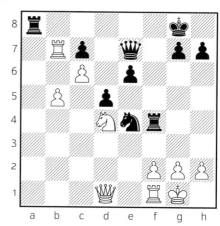

## (107)

▷ A. Korobov
► E. Sutovsky
Poikovsky, 2016.07.29

1. +-

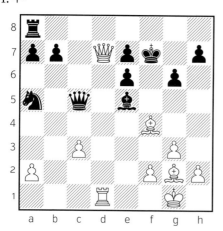

## (108)

▷ K. Sasikiran
► B. Stillger
Vlissingen Open, 2016.08.07

1. +-

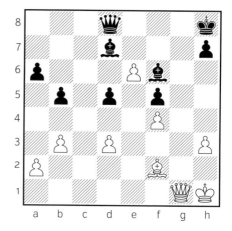

# (109)

▷ **F. Vallejo Pons**
► **Gonzalez de la S. Torre**
Spanish Championship, 2016.08.09

1. +−

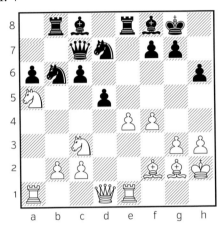

# (110)

▷ **A. Pirverdiyev**
► **C. Aravindh**
World Juniors, 2016.08.09

1... −+

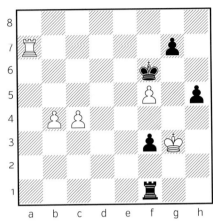

# (111)

▷ **Tran Tuan Minh**
► **K. Alekseenko**
Wolrd Juniors, 2016.08.13

1... −+

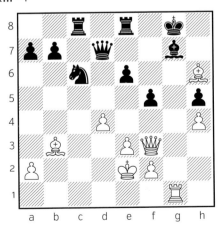

# (112)

▷ **M. Cornette**
► **S. Feller**
French Championship, 2016.08.17

1. +−

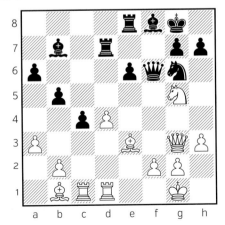

# (113)

▷ **B. Savchenko**
► **AlJ. Huwar**
Abu Dhabi Open, 2016.08.21

1. +-

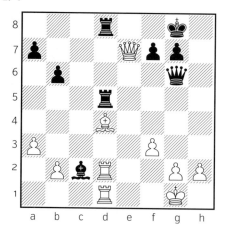

# (114)

▷ **A. Salem**
► **M. Siva**
Abu Dhabi Open, 2016.08.21

1. +-

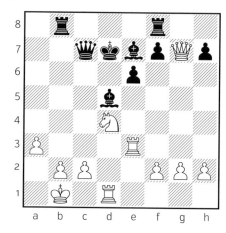

# (115)

▷ **H. Gusain**
► **Y. Kuzubov**
Abu Dhabi Open, 2016.08.22

1... -+

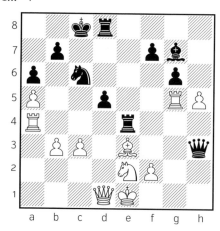

# (116)

▷ **Yu Yangyi**
► **Zhou Jianchao**
Chinese Rapid Champ., 2016.08.25

1. +-

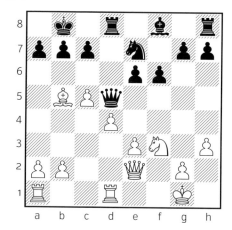

# (117)

▷ **Wang Hao**
► **M. Antipov**
Abu Dhabi Open, 2016.08.25

1. +-

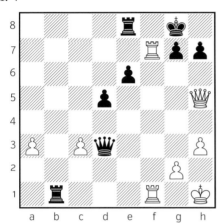

# (118)

▷ **O. Bortnyk**
► **Wang Hao**
Abu Dhabi Open, 2016.08.27

1... -+

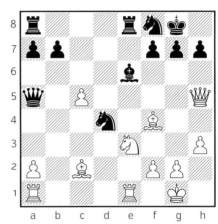

# (119)

▷ **H. Melkumyan**
► **S. Das**
Abu Dhabi Open, 2016.08.28

1. +-

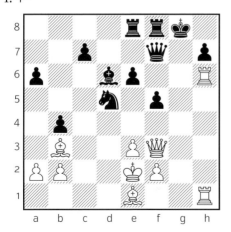

# (120)

▷ **Y. Wei**
► **B. Sadiku**
Olympiad, 2016.09.02

1. +-

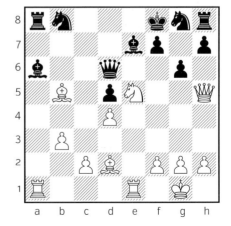

## (121)

▷ **S. Shankland**
► **J. Fernandez Lopez**
Olympiad, 2016.09.02

1. +-

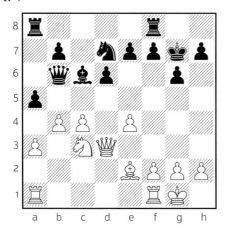

## (122)

▷ **A. Naiditsch**
► **S. Masango**
Olympiad, 2016.09.02

1. +/-

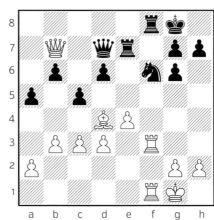

## (123)

▷ **A. Fejzullahu**
► **Li Chao**
Olympiad, 2016.09.02

1... -+

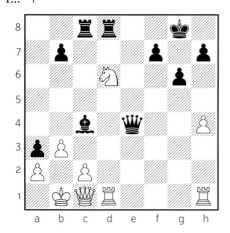

## (124)

▷ **D. Navara**
► **H. Stefansson**
Olympiad, 2016.09.03

1. +-

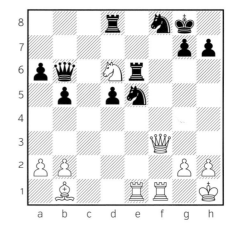

## (125)

▷ **N. Abasov**
► **T. Laurusas**
Olympiad, 2016.09.03

1. +−

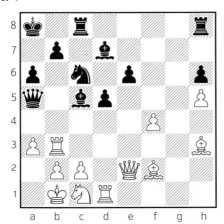

## (126)

▷ **A. Volokitin**
► **D. Fridman**
Olympiad, 2016.09.04

1. +−

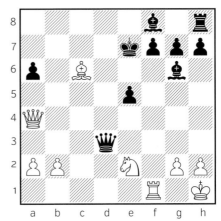

## (127)

▷ **S. Jessel**
► **Le Quang Liem**
Olympiad, 2016.09.05

1... −+

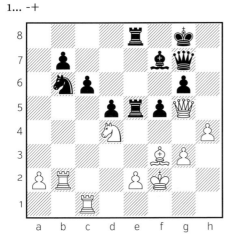

## (128)

▷ **H. Nakamura**
► **R. Markus**
Olympiad, 2016.09.06

1. +−

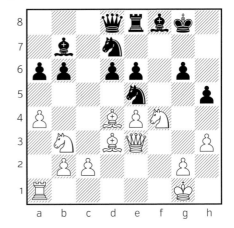

# (129)

▷ S. Minero Pineda
► E. Rozentalis
Olympiad, 2016.09.06

1... -+

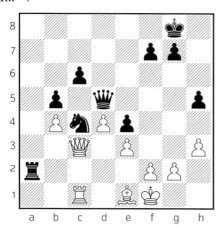

# (130)

▷ V. Durarbaily
► Y. Atabayev
Olympiad, 2016.09.06

1. +-

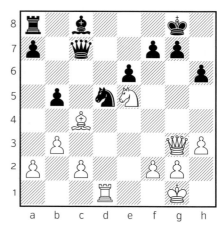

# (131)

▷ A. Rodriguez Vila
► R. Rapport
Olympiad, 2016.09.08

1... -+

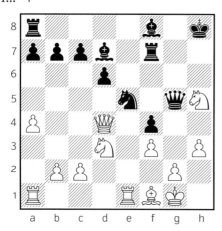

# (132)

▷ O. Jovanic
► M. Bosiocic
Trieste Open, 2016.09.08

1... -+

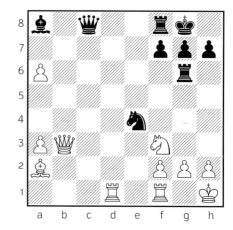

## (133)

▷ E. Torre
► A. Rombaldoni
Olympiad, 2016.09.09

1. +-

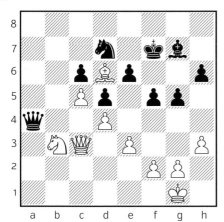

## (134)

▷ B. Jobava
► C. Lupulescu
Olympiad, 2016.09.09

1. +-

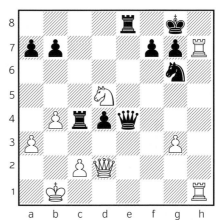

## (135)

▷ S. Tsolakidou
► V. Cmilyte
Olympiad Women, 2016.09.11

1... -+

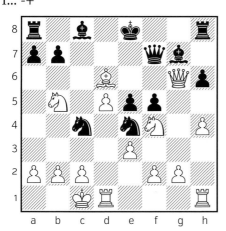

## (136)

▷ J. Goh Weiming
► J. Duda
Olympiad, 2016.09.11

1. +-

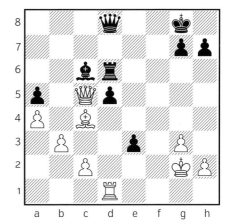

## (137)

▷ A. Tari
► S. Lorparizangeneh
Olympiad, 2016.09.12

1. +-

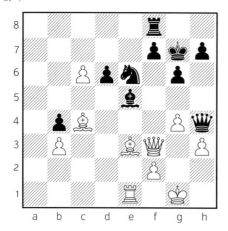

## (138)

▷ R. Wojtaszek
► F. Vallejo Pons
Olympiad, 2016.09.13

1. +-

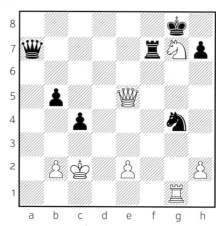

## (139)

▷ A. Hesham
► B. Amin
Baku Open, 2016.09.20

1. +-

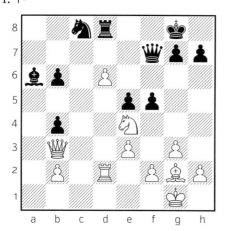

## (140)

▷ R. Edouard
► S. Cacho Reigadas
Spanish league, 2016.09.28

1. +-

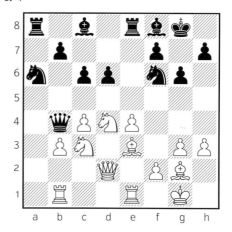

## (141)

▷ **L. Dominguez Perez**
► **B. Adhiban**
Spanish league, 2016.09.28

1. +-

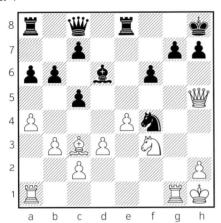

## (142)

▷ **Y. Kuzubov**
► **R. Rapport**
Spanish league, 2016.09.29

1. +-

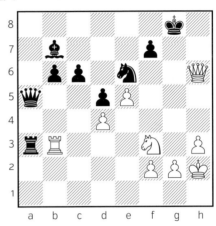

## (143)

▷ **Hou Yifan**
► **J. Jackson**
Isle of Man, 2016.10.01

1. +-

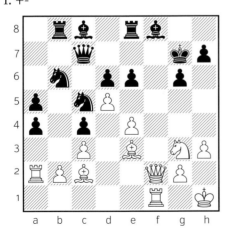

## (144)

▷ **B. Savchenko**
► **T. Salemgareev**
Russian Rapid Champ., 2016.10.02

1. +-

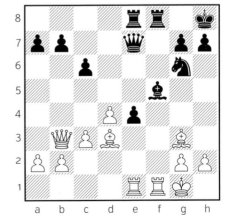

# (145)

▷ **D. Yuffa**
► **A. Riazantsev**
Russian Rapid Champ., 2016.10.03

1. +-

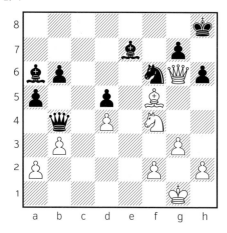

# (146)

▷ **V. Moiseenko**
► **I. Popov**
Russian Rapid league, 2016.10.05

1. +-

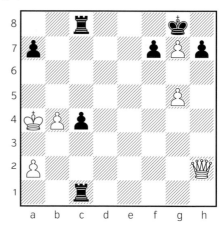

# (147)

▷ **Hou Yifan**
► **F. Caruana**
Isle of Man, 2016.10.06

1... -+

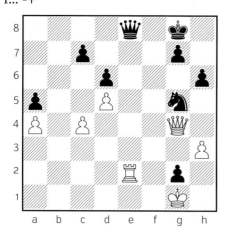

# (148)

▷ **S. Feller**
► **M. Bosiocic**
Croatian league, 2016.10.08

1. +-

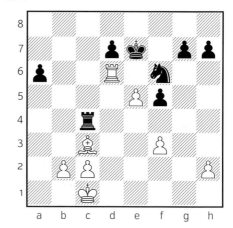

# (149)

▷ O. Wieczorek
► A. Korobov

German league, 2016.10.16

1. +-

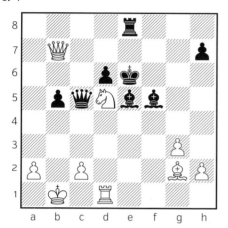

# (150)

▷ E. Enkhnar
► V. Kovalev

Chigorin memorial, 2016.10.18

1... -/+

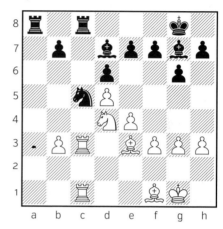

# (151)

▷ S. Mamedyarov
► R. Ponomariov

Amir Timur Rapid, 2016.10.19

1. +-

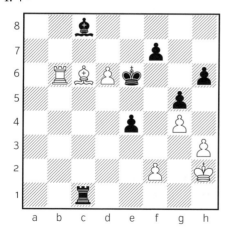

# (152)

▷ Hou Yifan
► N. Short

Match, 2016.10.22

1. +-

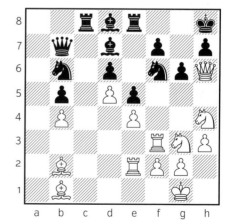

## (153)

▷ E. Rozentalis
► A. Volokitin
Austrian league, 2016.10.23

1. +−

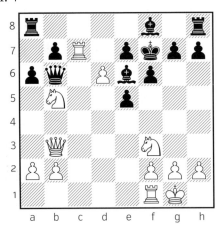

## (154)

▷ F. Bindrich
► D. Nisipeanu
Austrian league, 2016.10.23

1. +−

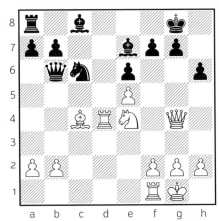

## (155)

▷ J. Hammer
► J. Salomon
Nordic Championship, 2016.10.24

1. +−

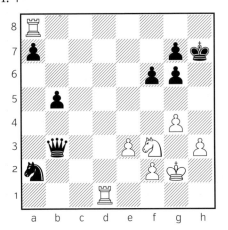

## (156)

▷ A. Korobov
► Hou Yifan
Corsican Circuit, 2016.10.28

1... −+

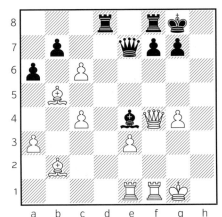

# (157)

▷ Y. Quesada Perez
► L. Figueredo Losada
Jugando Open, 2016.10.29

1. +-

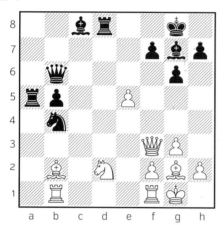

# (158)

▷ M. Petrosyan
► D. Shahinyan
Armenian Championship, 2016.11.04

1. +-

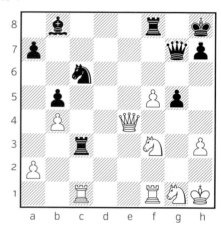

# (159)

▷ Wang Hao
► R. Gerber
European Club Cup, 2016.11.06

1. +-

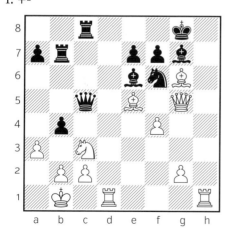

# (160)

▷ A. Predke
► J. Ahvenjarvi
European Club Cup, 2016.11.06

1. +-

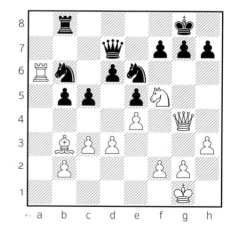

# (161)

▷ L. Van Wely
► F. Klein

European Club Cup, 2016.11.07

1. +-

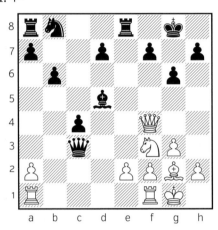

# (162)

▷ E. Blomqvist
► D. Dubov

European Club Cup, 2016.11.07

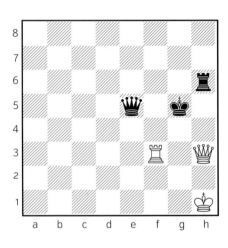

# (163)

▷ A. David
► S. Velickovic

European Club Cup, 2016.11.09

1. +-

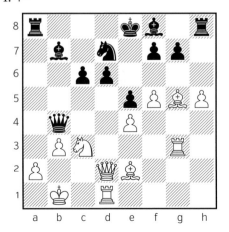

# (164)

▷ N. Vitiugov
► Λ. Huzman

European Club Cup, 2016.11.11

1. +/-

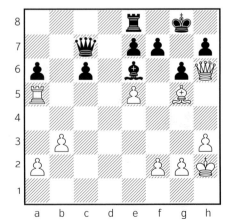

# (165)

▷ S. Stajner
▶ A. Beliavsky
Slovenian league, 2016.11.11

1. +−

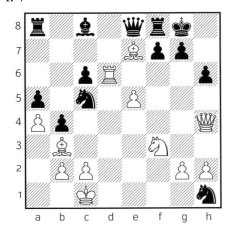

# (166)

▷ V. Ivanchuk
▶ B. Predojevic
European Club Cup, 2016.11.11

1. +−

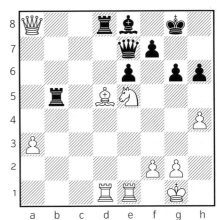

# (167)

▷ J. Van Foreest
▶ A. Lauber
European Club Cup, 2016.11.12

1. +−

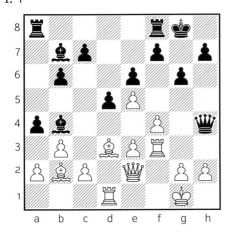

# (168)

▷ D. Semcesen
▶ H. Pohjala
European Club Cup, 2016.11.12

1. +−

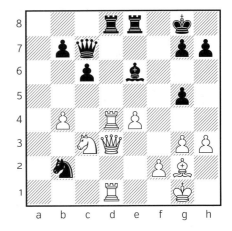

## (169)

▷ **A. Naiditsch**
► **A. Vovk**
Hungarian league, 2016.11.13

1. +-

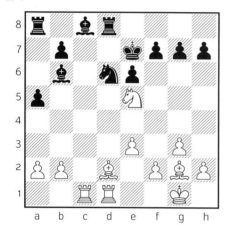

## (170)

▷ **V. Anand**
► **H. Nakamura**
Champions Showdown Rapid, 2016.11.13

1... =

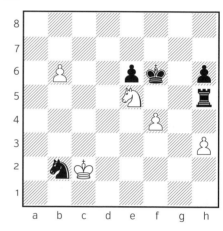

## (171)

▷ **D. Paravyan**
► **I. Rozum**
Ugra Cup, 2016.11.21

1... -+

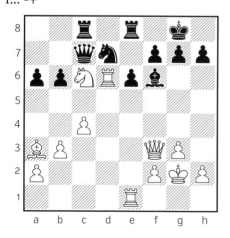

## (172)

▷ **M. Carlsen**
► **S. Karjakin**
WCC, New York, 2016.11.21

1... -+

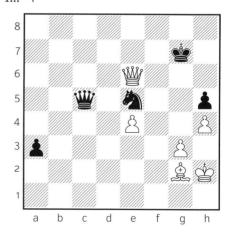

## (173)

▷ **K. Stupak**
▶ **A. Suleymenov**
Pavlodar Open, 2016.11.22

1... -+

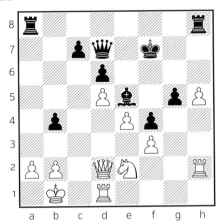

## (174)

▷ **D. Yuffa**
▶ **R. Ovetchkin**
Governor's Cup, 2016.11.24

1... -+

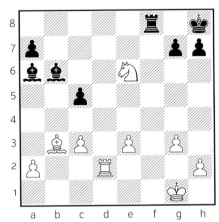

## (175)

▷ **M. Parligras**
▶ **V. Danilov**
Romanian league, 2016.11.25

1. +-

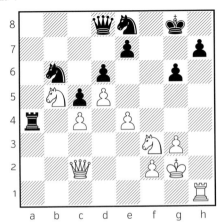

## (176)

▷ **F. Vallejo Pons**
▶ **D. Derakhshani**
R. Munichpid, 2016.11.26

1. +-

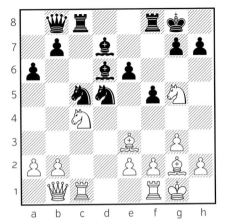

## (177)

▷ **K. Kulon**
► **Y. Shvayger**
Wroclaw, 2016.11.27

1. +-

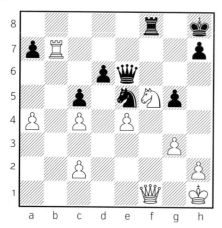

## (178)

▷ **N. Guliyev**
► **C. Tesik**
Hungarian league, 2016.11.27

1... -+

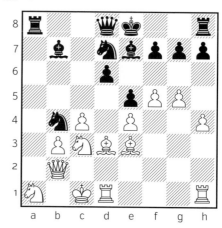

## (179)

▷ **V. Kramnik**
► **Hou Yifan**
10th Kings Rapid match, 2016.11.28

1. +-

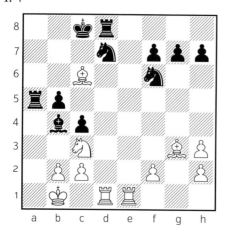

## (180)

▷ **Hou Yifan**
► **V. Kramnik**
Kings Blitz match, 2016.11.30

1. +/-

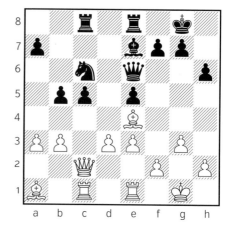

## (181)

▷ **M. Carlsen**
▶ **S. Karjakin**
WCC, New York tiebreak, 2016.11.30

1. +-

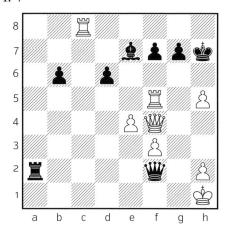

## (182)

▷ **P. Maletin**
▶ **S. Rublevsky**
Russian Rapid Cup, 2016.12.02

1. +-

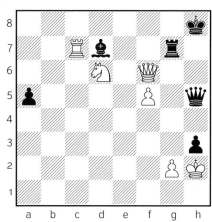

## (183)

▷ **S. Volkov**
▶ **E. Alekseev**
Russian Rapid Cup, 2016.12.03

1... -+

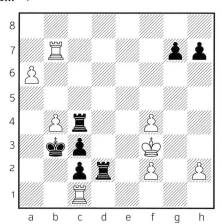

## (184)

▷ **V. Laznicka**
▶ **M. Kraemer**
German league, 2016.12.04

1. +-

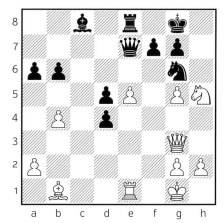

## (185)

▷ **A. Alonso Rosell**
► **C. Balogh**
French league, 2016.12.04

1... =

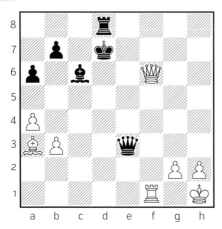

## (186)

▷ **K. Alekseenko**
► **P. Ponkratov**
Russian Cup, 2016.12.05

1. +-

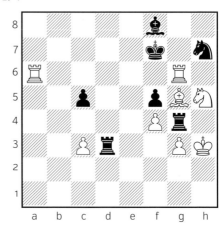

## (187)

▷ **M. Oleksiyenko**
► **A. Korobov**
Ukrainian Championship, 2016.12.10

1... -+

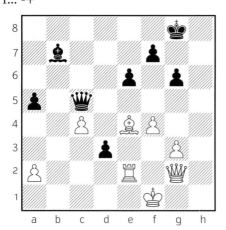

## (188)

▷ **A. Korobov**
► **A. Moiseenko**
Ukrainian Championship, 2016.12.14

1... -/+

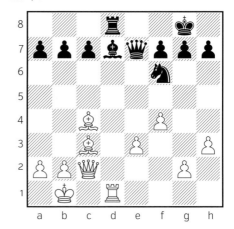

# – SOLUTIONS –

## [1]

▷ V. Mikhalevski
► V. Sveshnikov
Keres memorial rapid, 08.01.2016

22.d7! ♖xd7 [22...♖c7 23.♖dxc2 ♖xc2
24.♖xc2 ♗xb3 25.♖c8+-; 22...♖c6
23.♘a5+-] 23.♖cxc2 ♖xc2 24.♖xc2+-
[24.♖xc2 ♗xb3 25.♖c8++-]

## [2]

▷ Y. Krupenski
► B. Gelfand
Keres memorial rapid, 08.01.2016

27.♕g6+!! fxg6 28.♗g8+ ♔h8
29.♗f7+ 1–0

## [3]

▷ K. Georgiev
► E. Romanov
Keres memorial rapid, 08.01.2016

21.♖xd7! ♖xd7 22.♕xc6 ♔c8
23.♘e4! 1–0 [23.♘e4 ♕e5 24.♕a8#]

## [4]

▷ F. Berkes
► D. Lintchevski
Keres memorial rapid, 09.01.2016

91.♖d8+! ♔e7 92.h6!! 1–0 [92.h6
♔xd8 (92...gxh6 93.g7+-) 93.hxg7+-]

## [5]

▷ I. Popov
► A. Demchenko
Delhi Open, 12.01.2016

20.♗xc6! ♕xd1 [20...♗xf4
21.♖xe8++-] 21.♖axd1 bxc6
22.♗xe5±

## [6]

▷ Ma Qun
► R. Dive
New Zealand rapid, 12.01.2016

15.♗xf5! gxf5 16.♕h5+ ♔d7 17.♕xf5+
♔e8 18.♕h5+! ♔d7 19.♕h3+! 1–0
[19.♕h3+ ♔e8 20.♕xh8++-]

## [7]

▷ N. Torosyan
► R. Hovhanissyan
Armenian Championship, 15.01.2016

32...♖xe5! 33.dxe5 [33.♖xe5 ♗d2–+]
33...♗d2! 34.♖b3 [34.♖b1 ♗c3–+]
34...♗c1!–+ 0–1

## [8]

▷ K. Grigoryan
► L. Babujian
Armenian Championship, 15.01.2016

62...♖d2! 63.♖b7+ ♔f6 64.♖b6+
♔g7 65.a8♕ ♖xe2+ 66.♔h1 [66.♔g1
♘f3+ 67.♔f1 ♘xg3#] 66...♘xg3+
67.♔g1 ♘h3# 0–1

## [9]

▷ D. Nisipeanu
► N. Batsiashvili
Wijk aan Zee B, 16.01.2016

30.f5! gxf5 31.♗xf5! ♖d6 [31...♔xf5
32.♖f3#] 32.♗xh7+-

## (10)

▷ **T. Banusz**
▶ **K. Motuz**
Slovakian league, 17.01.2016

**23.♘d5+!! cxd5** [23...♔c8 24.♗xe5 ♘xe5 25.♘cb6+ ♔b8 26.♘xb4+−] **24.♘xe5+ ♘c5 25.♘d3+! gxf4 26.♘xb4** 1–0

## (11)

▷ **D. Shailesh**
▶ **Nguyen Huynh Minh Huy**
Chennai Open, 19.01.2016

**23.♘f6+!! gxf6 24.♘h5** 1–0 [24.♘h5 ♔h8 25.♕h6 ♖g8 26.♕xf6++−]

## (12)

▷ **B. Bok**
▶ **E. Safarli**
Wijk aan Zee B, 19.01.2016

**39...g5! 40.♗f6** [40.hxg5 h4−+] **40... gxh4 41.♗xh4 hxg4 42.fxg4 f5?!** [42... ♖b6−+] **43.♖xc4 dxc4 44.gxf5 ♖xf5∓**

## (13)

▷ **L. Van Wely**
▶ **M. Carlsen**
Wijk aan Zee A, 21.01.2016

**37...♖xf1+! 38.♔xf1 ♖d1+ 39.♔g2 ♗xe4−+** 0–1

## (14)

▷ **B. Adhiban**
▶ **A. Dreev**
Wijk aan Zee B, 23.01.2016

**21.♖xd7! ♕xd7 22.♗b5 ♕xb5 23.♕xb5+ ♔f8** [23...♔e7 24.♕e5+

**♔f8 25.♕d5 ♖c8 26.g3+−** h6 (*26...♗b2 27.♘g5+−; 26...f6 27.♘d4+−*) *27.♘e5+−*] **24.♕b3** 1–0 [24.♕b3 ♗d6 (*24...♗e7 25.♘e5+−*) 25.♘g5+−]

## (15)

▷ **H. Nakamura**
▶ **R. Bellin**
Gibraltar Open, 26.01.2016

**26.e6! ♘xe6 27.♗xg7+! ♔xg7 28.♕b2+! ♔g8 29.♖xc5 ♘xc5 30.♕b6+−**

## (16)

▷ **S. Mihajlov**
▶ **Ni Hua**
Gibraltar Open, 26.01.2016

**32...♖d1+! 33.♕xd1** [33.♔h2 ♘g4+−+] **33...♕xb8−+**

## (17)

▷ **M. Admiraal**
▶ **B. Bok**
Wijk aan Zee B, 26.01.2016

**30...♘xf2! 31.♖xf2 ♖e1+ 32.♘f1** [32. ♔h2 ♕xf2−+] **32...♖xf1+! 33.♔xf1 ♕d1#** 0–1

## (18)

▷ **E. Tomashevsky**
▶ **Ding Liren**
Wijk aan Zee A, 29.01.2016

**53...♖b1!−+** 0–1 [53...♖b1 54.♕xd6 (*54.♘f3 ♕xe5−+; 54.♕e4 ♖xe1+ 55.♕xe1 ♕xd4−+*) 54...♖xe1+ 55.♔g2 ♗xd6−+]

## (19)

▷ P. Vishnu
▶ B. Kohlweyer
Gibraltar Open, 01.02.2016

29.♗xe6! e3 [29...♗xe6 30.♕g5+
♔h7 31.♖xg7#; 29...♖a8 30.♕d2 ♖xa3
31.♕g5++-] 30.f3! ♖a8 31.♗xd5!
♘xd5 32.♖1b6+! ♔h7 [32...♘xb6
33.♕g5++-] 33.♗b2!!+-

## (20)

▷ L. Shytaj
▶ A. Donchenko
Gibraltar Open, 02.02.2016

26.♗g5! 1-0 [26.♗g5 ♖d7 27.♕h6+!
♔g8 28.♗f6+-]

## (21)

▷ L. Lenic
▶ R. Padmini
Gibraltar Open, 02.02.2016

28.♕xh6! 1-0 [28.♕xh6 gxh6
29.♘f6+ ♔g7 30.♘xd7++-]

## (22)

▷ Li Chao
▶ B. Uksini
Graz Open, 12.02.2016

24.♗xf7+! 1-0 [24.♗xf7+ ♖xf7
(24...♔xf7 25.♖d7++-) 25.♕g4+ ♕g6
26.♕xc8++-]

## (23)

▷ G. Kamsky
▶ D'L. Costa
Cappelle la Grande Open, 13.02.2016

25.♖xf7! ♗xf7 26.♖xf7! [26.e6!? ♗f8
27.♕g5 ♖xe6 28.♕f6 ♗g7 29.♕xe6+
♔h8 30.♖f7+-] 26...♔xf7 27.♕xh7+
♔e8 [27...♔e6 28.♕h3+ ♔f7 29.e6+
♔e8 30.♗xg6+ ♔d8 31.♕h8++-]
28.♕xg6++- ♔f8 29.♕h6+ ♔e8
30.♗b5+ ♕d7 31.♕g6+ ♔d8
32.♗b6+ 1-0

## (24)

▷ V. Anand
▶ L. Aronian
Zurich, 13.02.2016

15.♘xh6!! ♔xh6 [15...gxh6 16.♕xf6+-]
16.♕h3+ ♔g6 [16...♘h5 17.g4+-]
17.♖f3! ♘h5 18.♗f5! ♘f6 [18...♖h8
19.♕g4++-] 19.♕h4! 1-0 [19.♕h4 ♖h8
(19...♘h7 20.♕h5#) 20.♖g5#]

## (25)

▷ M. Daels
▶ E. Blomqvist
Cappelle la Grande, 17.02.2016

35...♗xh3+! 36.♔xh3 ♕f1+ 37.♔g4
♘e5+ 38.♔f5 ♕d3+! 0-1 [38...♕d3+
39.♗e4 ♕d7#]

## (26)

▷ G. Kamsky
▶ M. Kazhgaleyev
Cappelle la Grande, 18.02.2016

34.♘xe4! ♗g6 [34...fxe4 35.♕xe4+
♗g6 36.♕e6 ♘f6 37.♗e5!+-]
35.♕c6+-

## (27)

▷ N. Zhukova
► N. Pogonina
Tehran WGP, 22.02.2016

21.♘xg6!! fxg6 [21...hxg6 22.♕e5! f6 23.♕xe6+ ♗f7 24.♕xe7+-] 22.♕xe6+ ♗f7 [22...♔f8 23.♖xh7+-] 23.♕xe7 ♖xd4 24.♕h4 h5 25.♖xd4 ♕xd4 26.♖e3±

## (28)

▷ G. Kilgus
► B. Predojevic
Austrian league, 25.02.2016

15...♘c4! 16.♗c1 ♘a5! 0–1

## (29)

▷ S. Movsesian
► Li Chao
IMSA rapid, 26.02.2016

27...♖xb2! 28.gxf6 [28.♔xb2 a1♕+! 29.♖xa1 ♖b8+ 30.♔a2 ♕a5#] 28...♖xe2! 29.♖c1 [29.♗xe2 ♕c3+ 30.♔xa2 ♖a8+ 31.♔b1 ♖a1#] 29...♕b6 0–1 [29...♕b6 30.♗xe2 ♕d4+ 31.♔xa2 ♖a8+ 32.♔b1 ♖b8+ 33.♔c2 ♖b2#]

## (30)

▷ V. Ivanchuk
► R. Wojtaszek
IMSA blitz, 01.03.2016

63...♔xd7? [63...♖f8!! 64.♖xf8 ♔xd7 65.♔f6 ♗h5=] 64.♔xf6 1–0

## (31)

▷ V. Ivanchuk
► Ding Liren
IMSA basque, 02.03.2016

28...♘xd4+! 29.cxd4 b3+! 30.♔d2 ♖dxd4+ 0–1 [30...♖dxd4+ 31.♘d3 ♕a5+!–+]

## (32)

▷ B. Lalith
► A. Salem
Aeroflot Open, 08.03.2016

35...f2+! 36.♔xf2 [36.♕xf2 ♕xd1+] 36...g3+! 37.♔e1 [37.♔g1 ♕e3+ 38.♔h1 ♖h6–+] 37...♕c3+ 38.♖d2 ♖d8 39.♕e2 ♖xd2 40.♕xd2 ♕xc4–+

## (33)

▷ D. Dubov
► A. Moiseenko
Aeroflot Open, 08.03.2016

22.♘c7+!! ♕xc7 23.♗f7+ ♔f8 [23...♔e7 24.♕xg5+ ♔d6 25.♕d5+ ♔e7 26.♕xd4+-] 24.♕xg5+- ♕e5 25.♗xg6+ ♔g8 [25...♔g7 26.♖f7+ ♔g8 27.♕d8++-] 26.♗f7+! 1–0 [26.♗f7+ ♔f8 27.♗xh5++-]

## (34)

▷ M. Muzychuk
► Hou Yifan
World Championship, 09.03.2016

33...exf3! 34.♖xe7 ♖xe7 35.♖xe7 f2!–+

## (35)

▷ P. Meister
► R. Edouard
German league, 12.03.2016

22...♘e3! 23.♗xe3 [23.fxe3 ♕xe4 24.exd4 ♕d5∓] 23...♕xe4 24.♗g5 ♕b7–+

## (36)

▷ S. Karjakin
► H. Nakamura
Candidates, 12.03.2016

30.fxg3! ♘xd4 31.♗xd4 ♗xd4 32.exd4 ♕e3+ 33.♕f2! ♕xd3 34.♖c7!+-

## (37)

▷ K. Duda
► M. Rodshtein
German league, 13.03.2016

30.♖h7+! ♘xh7 [30...♔g8 31.♖h8+ ♔g7 32.♕h6#; 30...♔f8 31.♕h6+ ♔e7 32.♕g5+-] 31.♕xd7+-

## (38)

▷ S. Cicak
► N. Grandelius
Swedish league, 19.03.2016

25...♖xf2! 26.♖xf2 d3 27.♔f1 ♘xf2–+

## (39)

▷ P. Svidler
► H. Nakamura
Candidates, 23.03.2016

24...♖ae8! 25.♕xb6 ♖h4! 26.gxh4 ♕g4+ 1/2

## (40)

▷ R. Garcia Pantoja
► E. Cordova
Mexican Open, 24.03.2016

37.♕e6+! 1–0 [37.♕e6+ ♔h8 38.♕xc8! ♖xc8 39.♖d8+ ♖xd8 40.♖xd8#]

## (41)

▷ E. Cordova
► J. Flores Guerrero
Mexican Open, 24.03.2016

30.♖xg7+! ♔xg7 31.♘xe6+! ♔f6 32.♖xd7 ♔xe6 33.♖xb7 ♖xc4 34.♖xh7 ♖a4 35.h5+-

## (42)

▷ Li Chao
► V. Fedoseev
Grenke Open, 28.03.2016

27...♘xc4! 28.♘f5 [28.♘xc4 cxd5–+] 28...cxd5 29.exd5 ♗c8–+

## (43)

▷ M. Klekowski
► R. Wojtaszek
Polish Championship, 30.03.2016

14...♘c5 15.dxc5 dxe4 16.♕e3 [16. ♕xd8 ♖fxd8 17.♗e3 exf3 18.gxf3 ♘d7 19.♘a4 ♘e5∓] 16...exf3 17.♖fd1 fxg2∓

## (44)

▷ G. Popilski
► G. Kamsky
Calgary Open, 31.03.2016

10.♗xf7+! [10.e6?! ♕xf4 11.exf7+ ♔f8 12.fxg8♕+ ♖xg8 13.♗xg8 ♔xg8

14.0–0 ♖b8∞] **10...♔d8** [10...♔xf7
11.e6+ dxe6 12.♗xc7+–] **11.♕e2+–**

## (45)

▷ N. Murshed
▶ R. Jumabayev
Asian Nations Cup, 02.04.2016

**35.♘d6+!** ♗xd6 **36.♕f6+** ♔e8
[36...♔g8 37.♕xg6+ ♘g7 38.♘g5+–]
**37.♕xe6+** ♗e7 **38.♘f6+** ♔d8 **39.♗e5**
1–0

## (46)

▷ D. Swiercz
▶ M. Kanarek
Polish Championship, 05.04.2016

**20.♗xh6!!** ♗xh6 [20...cxd3 21.♘g5+
♔g8 22.♗xg7 ♔xg7 23.♕h7#]
**21.♘g5+!** ♔g7 **22.♖xf7+!!** ♖xf7
**23.♘xe6+** ♔h7 **24.♘xc7+–**

## (47)

▷ D. Svetushkin
▶ D. Dvirnyy
Karpos Open, 05.04.2016

**29.♖xe6!** ♖xe6 **30.c4** ♕g6 **31.♕b7!**
♖f7 **32.♕a8+** ♖f8 **33.♕xa7+–** 1–0

## (48)

▷ V. Jianu
▶ A. Dolana
Romanian Championship,
05.04.2016

**40...♖h1+!** **41.♔g3** ♘e4+! **42.♔h4**
♘d6–+

## (49)

▷ I. Khairullin
▶ V. Antonio
Bangkok Open, 13.04.2016

**17.0–0!** ♖xe4 **18.♕d5!** 1–0

## (50)

▷ F. Vallejo Pons
▶ Wynn Zaw Htun
Bangkok Open, 15.04.2016

**22.♖xe6+!** ♔xe6 **23.♘d5+–**

## (51)

▷ B. Jobava
▶ C. Krishna
Dubai Open, 16.04.2016

**31.g5!** hxg5 **32.♖xg5+!** ♗g6 **33.h6+!**
1–0

## (52)

▷ M. Vachier Lagrave
▶ P. Eljanov
Norway blitz, 18.04.2016

**35.a6!** bxa6 **36.♖a5!** 1–0

## (53)

▷ L. Pantsulaia
▶ S. Sethuraman
Dubai Open, 18.04.2016

**33.♗f6+!** 1–0 [33.♗f6+ ♔xf6 (33...
♔h7 34.♕g5+–) 34.♕h6#]

## (54)

▷ Gao Rui
▶ Y. Xu
Chinese Championship, 19.04.2016

32...♖a1+! 33.♔xa1 ♕a6+! 34.♔b1 ♕f1+ 0–1

## (55)

▷ **N. Guliyev**
► **L. Riemersma**
Dutch league, 23.04.2016

27.♖h8+!! ♔xh8 28.♕xf7 ♘f5 29.♖h1+ ♘h6 30.♕xg6+-

## (56)

▷ **H. Nakamura**
► **J. Xiong**
US Championship, 24.04.2016

31.♘xd4! ♗xb1 [31...cxd4 32.♗xd4 e5 33.♖e1+-] 32.♘f5! exf5 [32...♕f8 33.♘h6++-] 33.♗xg7+-

## (57)

▷ **A. Giri**
► **N. Grandelius**
Norway Chess, 28.04.2016

23.♘f6+! gxf6 24.♗xf6 ♕f5! [24...♔h7? 25.♕d3+! ♔g8 26.♖xe8+ ♕xe8 27.♘g5! hxg5 28.♕h3+-] 25.♕xh6 ♕h7 26.♕g5+ ♕g6 27.♕h4 ♕h7 1/2

## (58)

▷ **W. So**
► **H. Nakamura**
Ultimate Chess Challenge (blitz), 29.04.2016

27...♘xb4!! 28.♕xb4 [28.♘xb4 ♕d1#] 28...♕xc2-+

## (59)

▷ **G. Kasparov**
► **W. So**
Ultimate Chess Challenge (blitz), 29.04.2016

25...♗f5! 26.♖xe5 ♗xc2 27.♖d2 ♘xc4! 28.♖xc5 ♘xd2 29.♖xc2 ♖d8 30.♗xb7=

## (60)

▷ **S. Rublevsky**
► **D. Frolyanov**
Russian league, 03.05.2016

27.♖xh5! ♗a6 [27...♕xd4+ 28.♕xd4 exd4 29.♖h8+ ♔e7 30.♖e1++-] 28.♖h8+ ♔e7 29.♕g5+ f6 30.♕g7+ 1-0 [30.♕g7+ ♔e6 31.♕g4+ ♔e7 32.♖h7+ ♔d8 33.♗b6++-]

## (61)

▷ **V. Artemiev**
► **E. Inarkiev**
Russian league, 08.05.2016

33...♘xf2! 34.♖xf8+! [34.♔xf2 ♕xg3+-+] 34...♔xf8 35.♗xh6+ ♕xh6? [35...♔g8! 36.♕xf2 ♘xg3 37.♕xf3 ♘f5+∓] 36.♕xf2 ♕c1+ 37.♕f1?? [37.♘f1=] 37...♘xg3! 0-1 [37...♘xg3 38.♕xc1 ♘e2+ 39.♔f2 ♘xc1-+]

## (62)

▷ **A. Predke**
► **V. Yandemirov**
Russian league, 09.05.2016

13.♕e6! ♕xe6 [13...0-0-0 14.♕xb6 axb6 15.♘f7±] 14.♘c7+! ♔d8 15.♘gxe6+ ♔c8 16.♘xa8+-

## (63)

▷ M. Vachier Lagrave
► F. Caruana
Internet blitz, 10.05.2016

**30...♘d5! 31.♖xg7+ ♔f8!** 0–1

## (64)

▷ E. Inarkiev
► D. Svetushkin
European Championship, 13.05.2016

**24.♖xd8!!** ♖xd8 [24...♕xd8 25.♘f6+
♔g7 26.♕g5! ♘d7 27.♘gh5+ ♔h8
28.♕h6+-] **25.♘f6+ ♔g7 26.♕g5!**+-
♕c5+ [26...♘f3+ 27.gxf3 ♕xf6
28.♘h5++-] **27.♔h1 ♘d3 28.♘fh5+!**
[28.♘gh5+? ♔h8 29.♕h6 ♘f2+–+]
**28...♔g8 29.♕f6! ♘f2+** [29...♕e5
30.♗xf7++-] **30.♖xf2 ♖d1+ 31.♘f1
gxh5 32.♗xf7+ ♖xf7 33.♕xf7++-**

## (65)

▷ I. Cheparinov
► L. Pantsulaia
European Championship, 16.05.2016

**36.♘g6+!** [36.♖xd8! ♖xd8 37.♘d5!
♖xd5 (37...♕e6 38.♕g4+-) 38.♕e8++-]
**36...hxg6 37.♕h2+! ♔g8 38.♘h6+
♔g7 39.♖xf6+-**

## (66)

▷ E. Blomqvist
► E. Romanov
European Championship, 16.05.2016

**23...♖xa5! 24.♕xa5 ♖e2+ 25.♔f1
♗d3!** 0–1 [25...♗d3 26.♕a8+ (26.cxd3
♕xf3+–+) 26...♖e8+–+]

## (67)

▷ M. Gagunashvili
► D. Dubov
European Championship, 19.05.2016

**30...♘g3+!! 31.♔g1** [31.♗xg3 ♕xh3+
32.♗h2 ♕g2#] **31...♘e2+ 32.♔f2
♘xc1 33.♖xe6 ♘xf1!** 0–1

## (68)

▷ D. Navara
► A. Pashikian
European Championship, 23.05.2016

**32.♕d2! ♗c5 33.b4!+-**

## (69)

▷ A. Grischuk
► I. Kuznetsov
Kurnosov memorial, 26.05.2016

**19.♗e3! ♕e7 20.♗xg6! ♖xe5** [20...
hxg6 21.♕xg6+ ♕g7 22.♕xh5+-]
**21.♗e8+! ♕g7** [21...♔f8 22.♗xc6
bxc6 23.♕xe5+-] **22.♕xg7+** [22.♗h6!
♕xg3 23.fxg3 ♗f5 24.g4+-] **22...♔xg7
23.♗xc6 ♖xe3** [23...bxc6 24.♗d4+-]
**24.♗xb7 ♗xb7 25.fxe3+-**

## (70)

▷ A. Giri
► S. Karjakin
Shamkir, 27.05.2016

**35.f5! gxf5 36.♘f2! ♕g6 37.exf5 ♖xe2**
[37...♕f7 38.♖xe7 ♖xe7 39.♖xe7
♕xe7 40.♕xh5+-] **38.fxg6! ♖xe1
39.♕xh5 ♖h8 40.♕f3+-**

## (71)

▷ A. Fedorov
► D. Ospennikov
Nezhmetdinov memorial rapid,
28.05.2016

19.♗xh6! gxh6 20.♕xh6 ♘8h7
21.♘g5! ♕e7 22.♘xh7 ♘xh7 23.f6!
♘xf6 24.♖e3! 1–0

## (72)

▷ A. Sumets
► A. Naiditsch
French league, 30.05.2016

45...♖xh2+!! 46.♔xh2 ♕h8+!
47.♔g1 ♘e2+–+ 0–1

## (73)

▷ S. Mamedyarov
► E. Safarli
Shamkir, 02.06.2016

19.♖b5! ♗xb5 20.♖xb5 ♘xf2
21.♔xf2±

## (74)

▷ A. Timofeev
► A. Sharafiev
Nezhmetdinov memorial,
04.06.2016

28.♘xf6! ♔xf6 [28...♕xf6 29.♖xc7+
♔g8 30.♕xb4+– (30.♖f4+–)] 29.♕f4+
♔e7 [29...♔g7 30.♖xc7+ ♗d7
31.♕d6+–] 30.♖xe6+ ♔xe6 31.♖e3+
♔d7 32.♕f5+ 1–0 [32.♕f5+ ♔d6
33.♕e6#]

## (75)

▷ F. Caruana
► M. Carlsen
Grand tour, Paris rapid, 09.06.2016

13...♘xe4! 14.♗xe7 [14.dxe4
♗xg5–+] 14...♘c5! 15.♗d5 ♗xd5
16.♕xd5 ♕xe7∓

## (76)

▷ V. Kramnik
► F. Caruana
Grand tour, Paris rapid, 10.06.2016

54.♖a7+! [54.♖g8+?? ♔xg8 55.♕xh6
♖xf2+ 56.♔h3 ♗g2+ 57.♔h2 ♗f3+
58.♔g1 (58.♔h3 ♗g4#) 58...♖g2+
59.♔f1 ♖d1#] 54...♗d7 [54...♖d7
55.♖xd7+ ♗xd7 56.♖g8+! ♔h7
57.♖h8+! ♔xh8 58.♕xh6++–]
55.♖g8+! ♔xg8 56.♕xh6 ♖xf2+
57.♔h3+–

## (77)

▷ A. Giri
► L. Fressinet
Grand tour, Paris rapid, 10.06.2016

20.♘xd6+!! ♕xd6 [20...cxd6
21.♘xe4 ♕xe4 22.♖he1+–] 21.♘xe4
♕e7 22.♕d4 1–0

## (78)

▷ L. Fressinet
► V. Kramnik
Grand tour, Paris rapid, 10.06.2016

22...♘xh3! 23.gxh3 ♖xf3! 24.♖e2
[24.♕xf3 e4+–+] 24...♖af8–+

## (79)

▷ F. Caruana
► M. Vachier Lagrave
Grand tour, Paris rapid, 10.06.2016

**46...♘h3!** **47.♖xg4** [47.♖g3 ♘hf2+!
48.♔g1 ♘xd3–+; 47.♕xh3 ♘f2+
48.♔h2 ♕xg1#] **47...♕xg4–+**

## (80)

▷ W. So
► M. Carlsen
Grand tour, Paris blitz, 12.06.2016

**28...♕xd1+!** 0–1 [28...♕xd1+ 29.♗xd1
♖e1+ 30.♔g2 ♗f1+ 31.♔f3 (*31.♔g1
♗h3#*) 31...♘e5+ 32.♔f4 ♘xd7–+]

## (81)

▷ A. Giri
► M. Carlsen
Grand tour, Paris blitz, 12.06.2016

**22.♘xg7!!** **♕b7** [22...♔xg7 23.♖xd7!
♖xd7 24.♕g4+ ♗g6 25.♕xd7+–]
**23.♗d4!** **♗h1** **24.♕f2+–**

## (82)

▷ F. Caruana
► V. Anand
Grand tour, Leuven rapid, 17.06.2016

**9.♗xg8!** **♘d7** [9...♖xg8 10.♕c4!+–]
**10.♕b3+–**

## (83)

▷ A. Stefanova
► G. Jones
Eurasian blitz, 18.06.2016

**18...♕e5!** **19.♘xf8** **♕g3+** **20.♔d2**
[20.♔e2 ♕g2+–+] **20...♖d8+ 21.♔c2**

♕f2+ **22.♔b3** **♖xd1** **23.♖axd1**
**♗xf8–+**

## (84)

▷ S. Movsesian
► J. Van Foreest
Teplice Open, 18.06.2016

**23.♘d6!!** **♗xd6** [23...♘xf4 24.♕xf7+
♔h8 25.♘xe8 ♖xe8 26.♕xf4+–]
**24.♕xd5+–** 1–0

## (85)

▷ S. Karjakin
► V. Onischuk
Eurasian blitz, 18.06.2016

**43.♕e5+!** **♔xd7** **44.♗b5+** **♔d8**
**45.♕e8+** **♔c7** **46.♕c6+** **♔b8** [46...
♔d8 47.♕d7#+–] **47.♕e8+** **♔c7**
**48.♕d7+** **♔b8** [48...♔b6 49.♕c6+
♔a7 50.♕c7+ ♔a8 51.♗c6#]
**49.♕d8+** **♔b7** [49...♔a7 50.♕c7+
♔a8 51.♗c6#] **50.♗c6+** **♔a6**
**51.♕a5#** 1–0

## (86)

▷ A. Gabrielian
► A. Cherniaev
Russian Higher league, 27.06.2016

**22.♘e4!** **♕f4** [22...fxe4 23.♕xc5+
♕e7 24.♕xd4+–] **23.♘f6!** 1–0 [23.
♘f6 ♘f3+ 24.♕xf3! ♕xf3 25.♘d7+!
♔g7 26.gxf3+–]

## (87)

▷ V. Zvjagintsev
► A. Timofeev
Russian Higher league, 29.06.2016

**23.♗c1!** **♖d8** **24.♗h6±**

## (88)

▷ R. Kurbedinov
▶ D. Rodin
Russian Higher league, 29.06.2016

23...♞e5! 24.♕c3 ♞xd4! 25.♞xd4 ♖xd4! 26.♞g5 [26.♕xd4 ♞f3+–+] 26...♕d8–+

## (89)

▷ S. Volkov
▶ A. Predke
Russian Higher league, 01.07.2016

54.♔f6!! [54.♔f7? ♞e5+! 55.fxe5 ♖f1+–+] 54...h1♕ 55.♖g8+ ♔h7 56.♖g7+ ♔h6 [56...♔h8 57.♞g6#] 57.♞f5+ 1–0 [57.♞f5+ ♔h5 58.g4#]

## (90)

▷ A. Gorovets
▶ V. Bologan
World Open, 02.07.2016

47...♗b4!! 48.♖xa7 [48.♖a6+ ♔b5–+; 48.♗xb2 axb2!–+] 48...♖d2+ 49.♔e3 ♖xd4 50.♖xa3 [50.♔xd4 ♗c5+ 51.♔c4 ♗xa7–+] 50...♖h4–+

## (91)

▷ S. Pozo Vera
▶ S. Sevian
Annual World Open, 04.07.2016

28...♗xh3! 29.♗xh3 ♞g4+ 30.♔g2 [30.♔g1 ♕xh3–+] 30...♖h6! 31.♕e2 [31.♖h1 ♞e3+–+; 31.♗xg4 ♕h2+ 32.♔f3 ♕xc2–+] 31...♕xh3+ 0–1 [31...♕xh3+ 32.♔f3 ♕h5–+]

## (92)

▷ T. Sanikidze
▶ A. Mikaelyan
Batumi, 09.07.2016

74...♕f2+! 0–1 [74...♕f2+ 75.♔xf2 d1N+ 76.♔g3 ♞xb2–+]

## (93)

▷ G. Jones
▶ A. Puranik
Najdorf memorial, 09.07.2016

24...♖xb3! 25.cxb3 ♕xa3+ 26.♔b1 ♕xb3+ 27.♔c1 ♗e7!–+

## (94)

▷ P. Leko
▶ I. Nepomniachtchi
Danzhou, 11.07.2016

40...♞f2+! [40...♗xg1! 41.♞xc1 ♞f2+! 42.♔xg1 (42.♖xf2 ♗xf2 43.♞d3 ♗c5–+) 42...♖e1+ 43.♕f1 ♞h3+–+] 41.♖xf2 ♗xf2 42.♞xc1 ♗xg1 43.♕g3 [43.♕xg1 ♖e1–+] 43...♕d4 44.♕xg1 ♕d2–+ 45.♞d3 ♕xd3 46.♖g5 ♖e2 0–1

## (95)

▷ B. Savchenko
▶ Z. Bayramov
Alexandria Cup, 13.07.2016

29...e2! 30.♖xf4 [30.♗xe2 ♕e3+ 31.♔h1 ♕xe2 32.♖xf8+ ♗xf8–+] 30...e1♕+ 31.♖f1 ♕e3+ 32.♔h1 ♕xd3–+

## (96)

▷ B. Gelfand
▶ E. Inarkiev
Magas match, 14.07.2016

25.♕xf6! exd4 26.♘f5!+– dxe3
27.♖xd7 ♖xd7 28.♘xh6+ ♕xh6
29.♕xh6+–

## (97)

▷ Z. Efimenko
▶ M. Krasenkow
Najdorf memorial, 14.07.2016

29.♖xb6! 1–0 [29.♖xb6 ♕xb6
30.♕xa4! ♖xa4 31.♖c8++–]

## (98)

▷ B. Savchenko
▶ V. Danielyan
Aleksandria Cup, 15.07.2016

40.♖a8! ♖c7 [40...♖xa8 41.♕xd7+–;
40...♕xh3 41.♖xd8+ ♔g7 42.♘xh3+–]
41.♕xh7+! 1–0 [41.♕xh7+ ♕xh7
42.♖xd8+ ♔g7 43.♘xh7+–]

## (99)

▷ P. Leko
▶ V. Ivanchuk
Danzhou, 16.07.2016

51...♗g5? [51...♖c2+! 52.♔xb3 (52.
♔b5 b2–+) 52...♖b2+! 53.♔c4 (53.
♔a3 ♖a1#) 53...♖c1+ 54.♔d3 (54.♔d5
♖d2+–+) 54...♖c3+ 55.♔e4 ♖b4+
56.♔d5 ♖d4#] 52.f6! ♗xf6 53.♗d5=

## (100)

▷ K. Piorun
▶ B. Dubansky
Pardubice rapid, 20.07.2016

19.e4! dxe4 20.♕xh6 ♗f6 [20...♘d4
21.♘xd4 cxd4 22.♖xd4±] 21.♖xc5!+–

## (101)

▷ B. Gelfand
▶ E. Inarkiev
Magas match, 20.07.2016

23.f5! ♖e7 [23...dxe4 24.f6! ♕d7
25.f7++–] 24.♗g2! e4 25.♗a3+–

## (102)

▷ V. Onischuk
▶ J. Duda
Lake Sevan, 24.07.2016

22.♖xg7! ♔xg7 23.♗d4+ ♖f6
24.hxg4! ♘xg4 25.♗h3!+–

## (103)

▷ S. Ganguly
▶ V. Jansa
Pardubice, 24.07.2016

45.♖xg6! 1–0 [45.♖xg6 ♖xg6
46.♕h5+ ♖h6 47.♗g8+! ♔h8
48.♕xh6++–]

## (104)

▷ M. Matlakov
▶ V. Bologan
Poikovsky, 25.07.2016

28.♖xh7+! ♔xh7 29.♗g8+! ♔xg8
30.♕xd6 ♖c6 [30...♘f3+ 31.♔h1+–]
31.♕d5+ ♔g7 32.f4+–

## (105)

▷ G. Gaehwiler
▶ R. Jumabayev
Biel Open, 26.07.2016

14.♘db5! axb5 15.♘xb5 ♕c6
16.♕xe5! ♗g7 17.♘c7+ ♔f8
18.♘xa8+-

## (106)

▷ A. Dreev
▶ T. Ringoir
Xtracon Open, 26.07.2016

25.♖xc7! ♕xc7 26.♘xe6 ♕d6
27.♘xf4 ♕xf4 28.♕xd5+ ♔h8
29.c7+-

## (107)

▷ A. Korobov
▶ E. Sutovsky
Poikovsky, 29.07.2016

21.♖d5!! exd5 22.♗xd5+ ♔f8
23.♕e6! ♔e8 24.♗xe5+-

## (108)

▷ K. Sasikiran
▶ B. Stillger
Vlissingen Open, 07.08.2016

33.♗d4! ♗xd4 [33...♗xe6 34.♕g5!
♗xd4 35.♕xd8++-] 34.♕xd4+ ♔g8
35.♕xd5+-

## (109)

▷ F. Vallejo Pons
▶ Gonzalez de la S. Torre
Spanish Championship, 09.08.2016

21.♘xc6!! ♕xc6 22.exd5! ♖xe1
[22...♕d6 23.♖xe8+-] 23.dxc6 ♖xd1

24.♖xd1!+- g6 [24...♘f6 25.c7+-]
25.c7 ♖b7 26.♗xb7 ♗xb7 27.♘a4 1-0

## (110)

▷ A. Pirverdiyev
▶ C. Aravindh
World Juniors, 09.08.2016

40...h4+! 41.♔xh4 [41.♔g4 f2!
42.♔f3 h3! 43.♔g3 ♖g1+ 44.♔xf2
h2-+] 41...♖g1! 0-1 [41...♖g1 42.♖a2
♔xf5-+]

## (111)

▷ Tran Tuan Minh
▶ K. Alekseenko
Wolrd Juniors, 13.08.2016

27...♘e5!! 28.dxe5 [28.♖xg7+ ♕xg7
29.♗xg7 ♘xf3-+; 28.♕xh5 ♕b5+-+
29.♔e1 ♖c1+ 30.♔d2 ♖xg1-+] 28...
♕b5+ 29.♔e1 ♖c1+ 30.♗d1 [30.♔d2
♖xg1-+] 30...♖d8! 31.♖xg7+ ♔h8-+
32.♖g8+ ♖xg8-+

## (112)

▷ M. Cornette
▶ S. Feller
French Championship, 17.08.2016

28.♘xh7!! ♔xh7 29.♗g5! ♗d6 [29...
♕f7 30.♕g4! ♔g8 31.♕h5+-] 30.♕g4
1-0

## (113)

▷ B. Savchenko
▶ AlJ. Huwar
Abu Dhabi Open, 21.08.2016

32.♗xg7!! ♕e6 [32...♔xg7
33.♖xd5+-; 32...♖xd2 33.♖xd2 ♖xd2
34.♕f8+ ♔h7 35.♕h8#] 33.♕xe6

fxe6 34.♖xd5 exd5 35.♗f6 [35. ♖d2+-] 35...♗f8 36.♖c1+-

## (114)

▷ A. Salem
▶ M. Siva
Abu Dhabi Open, 21.08.2016

22.♘xe6!! fxe6 23.♖xd5+! ♔e8 [23... exd5 24.♖xe7++-] 24.♖xe6+- ♖f7 25.♕g8+ ♖f8 26.♕xh7+-

## (115)

▷ H. Gusain
▶ Y. Kuzubov
Abu Dhabi Open, 22.08.2016

25...♗xc3+! 26.♘xc3 ♖xe3+! 27.♘e2 [27.fxe3 ♕xe3+ 28.♘e2 ♕xg5–+] 27... ♕h1+ 28.♔d2 ♖d3+! 0–1

## (116)

▷ Yu Yangyi
▶ Zhou Jianchao
Chinese Rapid Championship, 25.08.2016

19.♘e5!! fxe5 20.dxe5 ♘g6 21.♖xd5+-

## (117)

▷ Wang Hao
▶ M. Antipov
Abu Dhabi Open, 25.08.2016

34.♖xg7+! ♔xg7 35.♕f7+ ♔h6 36.♕f4+! [36.♕f6+? ♕g6] 36... ♔h5 [36...♔g6 37.♕f6+ ♔h5 38.g4#; 36...♔g7 37.♕f6+ ♔g8 38.♕f7+ ♔h8 39.♕xe8++-] 37.♕g4+ ♔h6 38.♕h4+! 1–0 [38.♕h4+ ♔g7

39.♕f6+ ♔g8 40.♕f7+ ♔h8 41.♕xe8++-]

## (118)

▷ O. Bortnyk
▶ Wang Hao
Abu Dhabi Open, 27.08.2016

22...♘xc2! 23.♘xc2 ♕a4!–+ 0–1

## (119)

▷ H. Melkumyan
▶ S. Das
Abu Dhabi Open, 28.08.2016

31.♖xe6! ♖xe6 [31...♘f4+ 32.♕xf4! ♗xf4 33.♖xe8! ♖xe8 34.♗xf7+ ♔xf7 35.♖xh7+ ♔g6 36.♖h4 ♗e5 37.♖xb4+-] 32.♕xd5! ♖fe8 33.♖h6! c6 34.♕xe6 1–0

## (120)

▷ Y. Weii
▶ B. Sadiku
Olympiad, 02.09.2016

17.♗h6+! ♘xh6 18.♕xh6+ ♔g8 19.♗e8!+- 1–0

## (121)

▷ S. Shankland
▶ J. Fernandez Lopez
Olympiad, 02.09.2016

16.c5!! [16.b5 ♘e5] 16...♕c7 [16...dxc5 17.b5 ♘e5 18.♕g3+-] 17.cxd6! exd6 [17...♕xd6 18.♕xd6 exd6 19.b5+-] 18.♕d4+ ♘f6 19.b5+- 1–0

## (122)

▷ A. Naiditsch
► S. Masango
Olympiad, 02.09.2016

27.♕d5+!! ♕e6 [27...♘xd5 28.♖xf8#]
28.♗xf6 gxf6 29.♖xf6 ♖xf6
30.♖xf6 ♕xd5 31.exd5+-

## (123)

▷ A. Fejzullahu
► Li Chao
Olympiad, 02.09.2016

28...♖xd6! 29.♖xd6 ♗xb3! 30.axb3
a2+ 31.♔a1 [31.♔xa2 ♖xc2+−+] 31...
♕e5+ 32.♕b2 ♕xd6−+

## (124)

▷ D. Navara
► H. Stefansson
Olympiad, 03.09.2016

30.♖xe5! ♕xd6 [30...♖xe5 31.♕f7+
♔h8 32.♕xf8+ ♖xf8 33.♖xf8#]
31.♕f7+! [31.♖xd5 ♖f6!] 31...♔h8
32.♖xd5! 1−0 [32.♖xd5 ♕xd5
33.♕xf8+ ♖xf8 34.♖xf8#]

## (125)

▷ N. Abasov
► T. Laurusas
Olympiad, 03.09.2016

27.♖xb7!! 1−0 [27.♖xb7 ♔xb7
28.♘b3! ♕b5 29.♘xc5+ ♔c7 (29...
♔a8 30.♕xb5 axb5 31.♘xd7+-)
30.♘xa6+ ♔d6 31.♕xb5+-]

## (126)

▷ A. Volokitin
► D. Fridman
Olympiad, 04.09.2016

22.♖d1!! ♕xe2 23.♕b4+! 1−0 [23.
♕b4+ ♔f6 (23...♔e6 24.♗d7+ ♔f6
25.♕h4#) 24.♕h4+ ♔e6 25.♗d7#]

## (127)

▷ S. Jessel
► Le Quang Liem
Olympiad, 05.09.2016

31...f4! 32.♕xf4 ♖e4! 33.♗xe4
♕xd4+ 34.♕e3 ♕xb2 0−1

## (128)

▷ H. Nakamura
► R. Markus
Olympiad, 06.09.2016

22.♘xg6!! 1−0 [22.♘xg6 ♘xg6
23.♕g3 ♔h7 (23...♘de5 24.♗xe5 dxe5
25.♕xg6++-) 24.e5!+-]

## (129)

▷ S. Minero Pineda
► E. Rozentalis
Olympiad, 06.09.2016

48...♖a3! 49.♕c2 ♖xe3! 50.♗c3 [50.
fxe3 ♘xe3+ 51.♔e2 ♘xc2−+] 50...
♖d3−+

## (130)

▷ V. Durarbaily
► Y. Atabayev
Olympiad, 06.09.2016

21.♖xd5!! bxc4 [21...exd5 22.♗xd5
♗b7 23.♗xf7+ ♔h7 (23...♔f8 24.♘g6+

♔xf7  25.♕xc7++-)  24.♕d3++-]
22.♘xc4! ♕e7 [22...♕xg3 23.♖d8+
♔h7 24.fxg3+-] 23.♖d1+-

## (131)

▷ A. Rodriguez Vila
▶ R. Rapport
Olympiad, 08.09.2016

24...♗g7!! 25.♘xe5 [25.♘xg7 ♘xf3+!
26.♔h1 ♘xd4-+] 25...♗xe5 26.♕d5
♕xh5-+

## (132)

▷ O. Jovanic
▶ M. Bosiocic
Trieste Open, 08.09.2016

23...♖xg2! 24.♔xg2 ♘g5! [24...
♕g4+ 25.♔h1 ♘d2 (25...♘g5? 26.♖d3)
26.♖xd2 ♗xf3+ 27.♕xf3 ♕xf3+
28.♔g1] 25.♔g3 [25.♖d3 ♕h3+-+]
25...♗xf3-+

## (133)

▷ E. Torre
▶ A. Rombaldoni
Olympiad, 09.09.2016

28.♕a5!! ♕xb3 [28...♕xa5 29.♘xa5+-
] 29.♕c7+-

## (134)

▷ B. Jobava
▶ C. Lupulescu
Olympiad, 09.09.2016

41.♖xg7+! ♔f8 [41...♔xg7 42.♕h6+
♔g8 43.♘f6#] 42.♖g8+! ♔xg8
43.♘f6+ ♔g7 44.♘xe4+- ♖xe4
45.♕d3 1-0

## (135)

▷ S. Tsolakidou
▶ V. Cmilyte
Olympiad Women, 11.09.2016

17...exf4!! 18.♘c7+ ♔d8 19.♕xf7
♗xb2+ 20.♔b1 ♘c3# 0-1

## (136)

▷ J. Goh Weiming
▶ J. Duda
Olympiad, 11.09.2016

31.♕xc6!! ♕f8 [31...e2 32.♖xd5!+-
; 31...♖xc6 32.♖xd5 ♕f6 33.♖d8#]
32.♖xd5 [32.♗xd5+ ♔h8 33.♖f1+-]
32...♖xc6 33.♖d8+ ♖xc4 34.♖xf8+
♔xf8 35.bxc4+-

## (137)

▷ A. Tari
▶ S. Lorparizangeneh
Olympiad, 12.09.2016

29.♗xe6! 1-0  [29.♗xe6  fxe6
30.♕xf8+! ♔xf8 31.c7+-]

## (138)

▷ R. Wojtaszek
▶ F. Vallejo Pons
Olympiad, 13.09.2016

35.♘e6! [35.♖xg4? ♕a4+∞] 35...
h5 [35...♖xg1 36.♕b8++-] 36.♕g5+
♔h7 37.♕xh5+ 1-0

## (139)

▷ A. Hesham
▶ B. Amin
Baku Open, 20.09.2016

27.♘f6+! 1-0 [27.♘f6+ gxf6 28.♗d5+-]

## (140)

▷ R. Edouard
► S. Cacho Reigadas
Spanish league, 28.09.2016

**20.♘c2! ♛a5 21.♘d5!** 1–0 [21.♘d5
♛d8 (21...♛xd2 22.♘xf6+ ♔g7
23.♘xe8+ ♔g8 24.♗xd2+–) 22.♗b6+–]

## (141)

▷ L. Dominguez Perez
► B. Adhiban
Spanish league, 28.09.2016

**26.♛h6!! ♘e6** [26...gxh6 27.♗xf6#;
26...♖e7 27.♗xf6+–] **27.♗xf6** [27.
♖xg7 ♘xg7 28.♘g5!+–] **27...♗f8
28.♖xg7! ♗xg7 29.♘g5!+–**

## (142)

▷ Y. Kuzubov
► R. Rapport
Spanish league, 29.09.2016

**36.♘g5! ♘xg5** [36...♖xb3 37.♛h7+
♔f8 38.♛xf7#] **37.♛xg5+ ♔f8** [37...
♔h7 38.♛h4+ ♔g7 39.♛g3+! ♔h7
40.♖xa3+–] **38.♛d8+ ♔g7 39.♛f6+
♔g8 40.e6! fxe6** [40...♖xb3 41.♛xf7+
♔h8 42.e7+–] **41.♛xe6+** 1–0 [41.
♛xe6+ ♔g7 42.♛e7++–]

## (143)

▷ Hou Yifan
► J. Jackson
Isle of Man, 01.10.2016

**31.♘h5+! gxh5** [31...♔h8 32.♛xf8+!
♖xf8 33.♖xf8#] **32.♗h6+! ♔xh6**
[32...♔g8 33.♛xf8+! ♖xf8 34.♖xf8#]
**33.♛f6#** 1–0

## (144)

▷ B. Savchenko
► T. Salemgareev
Russian Rapid Championship,
02.10.2016

**20.♖xf5! ♖xf5 21.♖xe4! ♘e5** [21...
♛f8 22.♖xe8 ♛xe8 23.♗xf5 ♛e3+
24.♔f1+–] **22.♖xe5 ♖xe5 23.♗xe5+–**

## (145)

▷ D. Yuffa
► A. Riazantsev
Russian Rapid Championship,
03.10.2016

**33.♛h7+!!** 1–0 [33.♛h7+ ♘xh7
34.♘g6+ ♔g8 35.♗e6#]

## (146)

▷ V. Moiseenko
► I. Popov
Russian Rapid league, 05.10.2016

**39.g6! fxg6** [39...hxg6 40.♛h8#]
**40.♛e5!+– ♖f1 41.♛e6+ ♔xg7
42.♛xc8+–**

## (147)

▷ Hou Yifan
► F. Caruana
Isle of Man, 06.10.2016

**29...♛xe2!** [29...♘xh3+? 30.♛xh3
♛xe2 31.♛c8+ ♔h7 32.♛f5+=]
**30.♛xe2 ♘xh3+ 31.♔h2** [31.♔xg2
♘f4+ 32.♔f3 ♘xe2–+] **31...g1♛+
32.♔xh3 ♛h7–+**

## (148)

▷ S. Feller
► M. Bosiocic
Croatian league, 08.10.2016

24.♖d4‼ 1–0 [24.♖d4 ♖xd4 25.exf6+ ♔xf6 26.♗xd4++-]

## (149)

▷ O. Wieczorek
► A. Korobov
German league, 16.10.2016

35.♘c7+! ♔f6 36.♘xe8+ ♔g6 37.♖xd6+! 1–0 [37.♖xd6+ ♗xd6 38.♕g7+ ♔h5 39.♘f6#]

## (150)

▷ E. Enkhnar
► V. Kovalev
Chigorin memorial, 18.10.2016

23...♗xd4! 24.♗xd4 ♘xb3! 25.♖xc8+ ♗xc8∓

## (151)

▷ S. Mamedyarov
► R. Ponomariov
Amir Timur Rapid, 19.10.2016

38.d7! ♗xd7 39.♗a4+! 1–0 [39.♗a4+ ♔e7 40.♖b7+-]

## (152)

▷ Hou Yifan
► N. Short
Match, 22.10.2016

29.♖xf6! ♗xf6 30.♘h5 gxh5 31.♕xf6+ ♔g8 32.♖e3!+-

## (153)

▷ E. Rozentalis
► A. Volokitin
Austrian league, 23.10.2016

20.♘xe5+! fxe5 21.♕f3+ ♔g8 22.♖xb7 ♕a5 23.♘c7+-

## (154)

▷ F. Bindrich
► D. Nisipeanu
Austrian league, 23.10.2016

17.♘f6+! ♔f8 [17...♗xf6 18.exf6+-] 18.♕xg7+! 1–0 [18.♕xg7+ ♔xg7 19.♖g4+ ♔f8 20.♖g8#]

## (155)

▷ J. Hammer
► J. Salomon
Nordic Championship, 24.10.2016

29.♘g5+‼ 1–0 [29.♘g5+ fxg5 (29...♔h6 30.♖h8+ ♔xg5 31.f4#) 30.♖dd8+-]

## (156)

▷ A. Korobov
► Hou Yifan
Corsican Circuit, 28.10.2016

27...♖d2! 28.♗f6 [28.♖f2 ♕h4! 29.♖xd2 ♕h1+ 30.♔f2 ♕g2#] 28...♖g2+ 29.♔h1 gxf6-+

## (157)

▷ Y. Quesada Pereza
► L. Figueredo Losada
Jugando Open, 29.10.2016

21.e6! 1–0 [21.e6 ♗xe6 22.♗xg7 ♔xg7 23.♖xb4 ♖xd2 24.♕c3+-]

## (158)

▷ M. Petrosyan
▶ D. Shahinyan
Armenian Championship, 04.11.2016

**33.f6!** ♕xf6 **34.**♖xc3 [34.♘xg5+−] **34...**♘e5 [34...♕xc3 35.♘xg5! ♖xf1 36.♕xh7#] **35.**♘xg5 1−0

## (159)

▷ Wang Hao
▶ R. Gerber
European Club Cup, 06.11.2016

**22.**♖h7!! bxc3 [22...♘xh7 23.♗xh7+ ♔xh7 24.♕xg7#] **23.**♗xf7+! ♔xh7 [23...♔xf7 24.♕xg7+ ♔e8 25.♖h8++−] **24.**♖h1+ 1−0

## (160)

▷ A. Predke
▶ J. Ahvenjarvi
European Club Cup, 06.11.2016

**26.**♘xg7!! ♘xg7 **27.**♖xb6! ♕c7 [27...♕xg4 28.♖xb8++−; 27...♖xb6 28.♕xd7+−] **28.**♖xb8+ ♕xb8 **29.**♕d7+−

## (161)

▷ L. Van Wely
▶ F. Klein
European Club Cup, 07.11.2016

**18.**♘g5! ♕e5 **19.**♗xd5 ♕xd5 **20.**e4!+− 1−0

## (162)

▷ E. Blomqvist
▶ D. Dubov
European Club Cup, 07.11.2016

**59.**♖g3+! ♕xg3 **60.**♕xh6+ ♔xh6= 1/2

## (163)

▷ A. David
▶ S. Velickovic
European Club Cup, 09.11.2016

**33.**♘b5! ♕xe4+ [33...♕xd2 34.♘c7#; 33...cxb5 34.♕xb4+−] **34.**♗d3 ♕xd3+ [34...cxb5 35.♗xe4 ♗xe4+ 36.♔b2+−] **35.**♖xd3 cxb5 **36.**♖xd6 1−0

## (164)

▷ N. Vitiugov
▶ A. Huzman
European Club Cup, 11.11.2016

**40.f4!** ♕d8 [40...♕xa5 41.♗f6! exf6 42.exf6+−] **41.**♖xa6+−

## (165)

▷ S. Stajner
▶ A. Beliavsky
Slovenian league, 11.11.2016

**22.**♖xh6! ♘xb3+ **23.**cxb3 gxh6 **24.**♗f6! ♔h7 **25.**♕e4+! ♔g8 **26.**♘g5! 1−0 [26.♘g5 hxg5 27.♕e3!+−]

## (166)

▷ V. Ivanchuk
▶ B. Predojevic
European Club Cup, 11.11.2016

**28.**♘c6! ♗xc6 **29.**♕xc6 ♖c5 [29... ♖bxd5 30.♖xd5 ♖xd5 31.♕xd5! exd5 32.♖xe7+−] **30.**♖xe6! 1−0 [30. ♖xe6 fxe6 31.♕xe6+ ♕xe6 (31...♔f8 32.♕g8#) 32.♗xe6+ ♔g7 33.♖xd8+−]

## (167)

▷ J. Van Foreest
► A. Lauber
European Club Cup, 12.11.2016

**17.a3!** 1–0 [17.c3+–; 17.a3 ♗c5 18.b4 ♗e7 19.♖h3+–]

## (168)

▷ D. Semcesen
► H. Pohjala
European Club Cup, 12.11.2016

**28.♖xd8!** ♘xd3 **29.♖xe8+** ♔f7 **30.♖xe6!** ♔xe6 **31.♖xd3+–**

## (169)

▷ A. Naiditsch
► A. Vovk
Hungarian league, 13.11.2016

**16.♖c6!** bxc6 **17.♘xc6+** ♔e8 **18.♘xd8** ♖a6 **19.♘c6+–**

## (170)

▷ V. Anand
► H. Nakamura
Champions Showdown Rapid, 13.11.2016

**52...♘c4?** [52...♘d3! 53.♔xd3 (53.b7? ♘b4+! 54.♔b3 ♘a6–+) 53...♖xh3+ 54.♔c4 ♖h1 55.b7 ♖b1 56.♘d7+ ♔f5=] **53.b7+–**

## (171)

▷ D. Paravyan
► I. Rozum
Ugra Cup, 21.11.2016

**22...♗b2!!** **23.♗xb2** [23.♖xd7 ♕xd7 24.♗xb2 ♕xc6–+; 23.♗b4 a5 24.♖ed1 axb4 25.♖xd7 ♕xc6–+] **23... ♕xd6–+**

## (172)

▷ M. Carlsen
► S. Karjakin
WCC, New York, 21.11.2016

**52...a2!** 0–1 [52...a2 53.♕xa2 ♘g4+ 54.♔h3 ♕g1 55.♕b2+ ♔g6–+]

## (173)

▷ K. Stupak
► A. Suleymenov
Pavlodar Open, 22.11.2016

**25...♖xa2!** **26.♘c1** [26.♔xa2 ♕a4+ 27.♔b1 ♖a8! (27...b3? 28.♘c3) 28.♕c1 (28.♘d4 b3–+; 28.♖c1 b3 29.♖xc7+ ♔f6–+) 28...c5! 29.dxc6 b3–+] **26... ♖xb2+ 27.♕xb2 ♗xb2–+**

## (174)

▷ D. Yuffa
► R. Ovetchkin
Governor's Cup, 24.11.2016

**29...c4!** **30.♘xf8** ♗xe3+ **31.♖f2 cxb3 32.axb3 ♗c8! 33.♔g2 ♗xf2 34.♔xf2 ♔g8–+**

## (175)

▷ M. Parligras
► V. Danilov
Romanian league, 25.11.2016

**23.♖xh7!!** ♖xc4 [23...♔xh7 24.♘g5+ ♔g8 (24...♔h6 25.♘f7++–; 24...♔g7 25.♘e6++–; 24...♔h8 25.♘f7++–)

25.e5!+-] **24.♕d2! ♘f6** [24...♔xh7
25.♘g5+ ♔g8 26.♘e6 ♕d7 27.♕h6+-]
**25.♖h6+-**

## (176)

▷ **F. Vallejo Pons**
▶ **D. Derakhshani**
Munich, Rapid, 26.11.2016

**17.♗xd5! exd5 18.♘b6 1 0** [18.♘b6
♖c7 19.♗xc5 ♗xc5 20.♖xc5 ♖xc5
21.♘xd7+-]

## (177)

▷ **K. Kulon**
▶ **Y. Shvayger**
Wroclaw, 27.11.2016

**31.♖xh7+!! ♔xh7 32.♕h3+ ♔g6**
[32...♔g8 33.♘h6+ ♕xh6 34.♕xh6
♖f1+ 35.♔g2 ♖f2+ 36.♔g1!+-]
**33.♕h6+ ♔f7 34.♕h7+! ♔e8** [34...
♔f6 35.♕g7#] **35.♘g7++-**

## (178)

▷ **N. Guliyev**
▶ **C. Tesik**
Hungarian league, 27.11.2016

**22...d5! 23.♗b1** [23.exd5 ♘xd3+
24.♖xd3 ♗a3-+] **23...♘d3+?** [23...
d4-+] **24.♖xd3 ♗a3 25.exd5∞**

## (179)

▷ **V. Kramnik**
▶ **Hou Yifan**
10th Kings Rapid match, 28.11.2016

**21.♘xb5! ♗xe1 22.♘d6+ ♔c7
23.♘xf7+ ♔xc6 24.♘xd8+ ♔b5
25.♖xe1+-**

## (180)

▷ **Hou Yifan**
▶ **V. Kramnik**
Kings Blitz match, 30.11.2016

**27.d4!! ♘a5** [27...cxd4 28.♗h7+ ♔h8
29.♗f5 ♕d5 30.♗xc8 ♖xc8 31.exd4+-
] **28.♗h7+ ♔h8 29.♗f5 ♕xb3
30.♗xc8±**

## (181)

▷ **M. Carlsen**
▶ **S. Karjakin**
WCC, New York tiebreak, 30.11.2016

**50.♕h6+!! 1-0** [50.♕h6+ gxh6 (50...
♔xh6 51.♖h8#) 51.♖xf7#]

## (182)

▷ **P. Maletin**
▶ **S. Rublevsky**
Russian Rapid Cup, 02.12.2016

**41.g4! ♕xg4 42.♘f7+! ♔h7** [42...
♔g8 43.♘h6++-] **43.♕h6+ ♔g8
44.♕h8+ ♔xf7 45.♖xd7+ ♔f6
46.♕f8++- 1-0**

## (183)

▷ **S. Volkov**
▶ **E. Alekseev**
Russian Rapid Cup, 03.12.2016

**37...♖d1! 38.a7 ♖xc1! 39.a8♕ ♖b1-+**

## (184)

▷ **V. Laznicka**
▶ **M. Kraemer**
German league, 04.12.2016

**27.♘f6+! gxf6 28.gxf6 ♕f8 29.♗xg6
fxg6 30.♕xg6+ ♔h8 31.♕h5+ ♔g8**

32.♖f1!+- ♕f7 [32...♗e6 33.♕g6+ ♔h8 34.♖f4+-] **33.♕g5+ ♔f8 34.♕h6+ ♔g8 35.♖f3** 1–0

## (185)

▷ **A. Alonso Rosell**
► **C. Balogh**
French league, 04.12.2016

37...♗xg2+! 38.♔xg2 ♖g8+ 39.♔h1 ♖g1+! 40.♖xg1 ♕e4+ 41.♖g2 ♕e1+= 1/2

## (186)

▷ **K. Alekseenko**
► **P. Ponkratov**
Russian Cup, 05.12.2016

43.♖af6+! ♘xf6 44.♖xf6+ ♔e8 45.♖xf5 ♖xg5 46.fxg5!+- c4 47.g6 1–0

## (187)

▷ **M. Oleksiyenko**
► **A. Korobov**
Ukrainian Championship, 10.12.2016

42...♕xc4!! 43.♗xb7 [43.♖d2 ♕c1++; 43.♖e1 d2+-+] **43...d2! 44.♕e4 d1♕+-+**

## (188)

▷ **A. Korobov**
► **A. Moiseenko**
Ukrainian Championship, 14.12.2016

18...♗c6?= [18...♗f5!! 19.♗d3 (19.♖xd8+ ♕xd8 20.♕xf5 ♕d1#) 19...♖xd3! 20.♖xd3 ♘d5∓]

## (1)

▷ **M. Rodshtein**
▶ **A. Donchenko**
Rilton Cup, 2016.01.04

1. +-

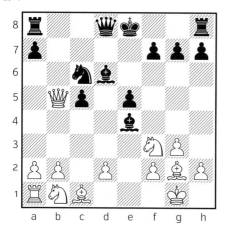

## (2)

▷ **S. Mamedyarov**
▶ **L. Van Wely**
Wijk aan Zee A, 2016.01.16

1... -+

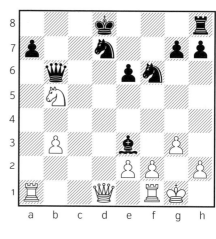

## (3)

▷ **I. Popov**
▶ **M. Kunal**
Chennai Open, 2016.01.20

1. +-

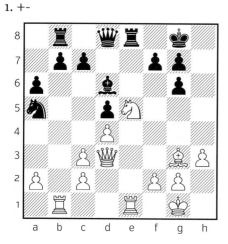

## (4)

▷ **D. Nisipeanu**
▶ **A. Haast**
Wijk aan Zee B, 2016.01.23

1... -+

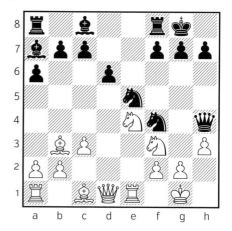

## (5)

▷ **A. Tukhaev**
► **C. Deepan**
Chennai Open, 2016.01.25

1. +-

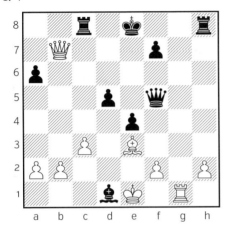

## (6)

▷ **J. Van Foreest**
► **B. Bok**
Wijk aan Zee B, 2016.01.27

1. +-

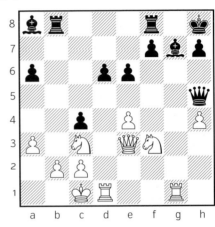

## (7)

▷ **N. Short**
► **D. Harika**
Gibraltar Open, 2016.01.28

1... -+

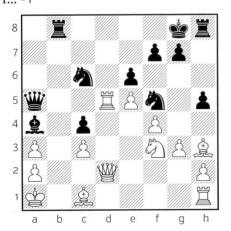

## (8)

▷ **M. Muzychuk**
► **R. Rapport**
Gibraltar Open, 2016.02.02

1... -+

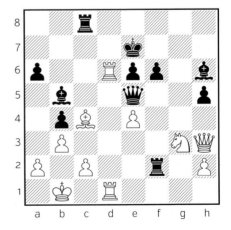

## (9)

▷ **S. Vidit**
► **A. Pichot**
Gibraltar Open, 2016.02.03

1. +-

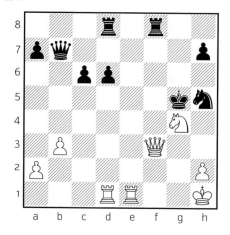

## (10)

▷ **A. Shirov**
► **H. Nakamura**
Zurich, 2016.02.13

1... -+

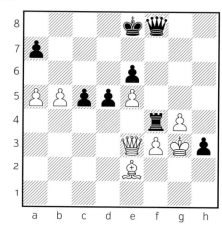

## (11)

▷ **G. Sarakauskas**
► **D. Howell**
4NCL, 2016.02.14

1... -+

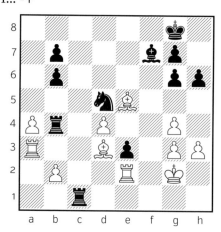

## (12)

▷ **E. Postny**
► **P. Schreiner**
Graz Open, 2016.02.15

1. +-

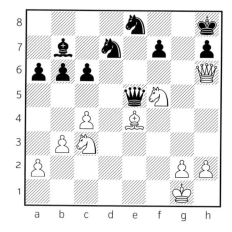

# (13)

▷ **L. Aronian**
► **V. Kramnik**
Zurich blitz, 2016.02.15

1. +-

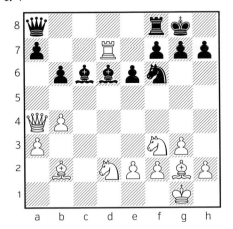

# (14)

▷ **D. Harika**
► **A. Stefanova**
Tehran WGP, 2016.02.16

1. +-

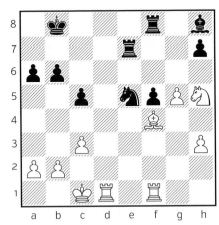

# (15)

▷ **R. Wojtaszek**
► **V. Ivanchuk**
IMSA rapid, 2016.02.26

1. +-

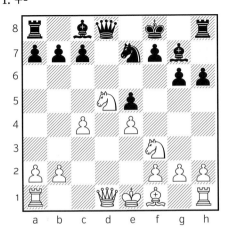

# (16)

▷ **R. Wojtaszek**
► **P. Harikrishna**
IMSA blitz, 2016.02.29

1. +-

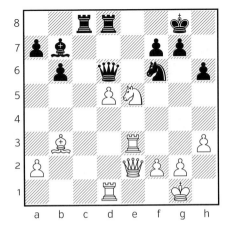

## (17)

▷ **R. Ponomariov**
► **Wang Yue**
IMSA blitz, 2016.02.29

1. +-

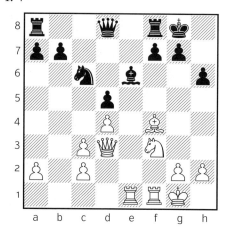

## (18)

▷ **Li Chao**
► **Wang Hao**
IMSA blitz, 2016.02.29

1. +-

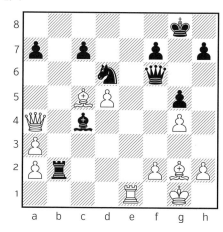

## (19)

▷ **Hou Yifan**
► **M. Muzychuk**
World Championship, 2016.03.03

1. +-

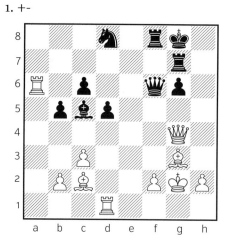

## (20)

▷ **Hou Yifan**
► **M. Muzychuk**
World Championship, 2016.03.06

1... =

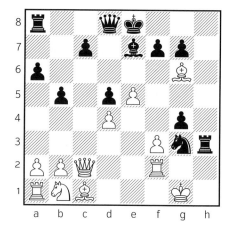

# (21)

▷ **V. Artemiev**
► **T. Petrosian**
Aeroflot Open, 2016.03.08

1. =

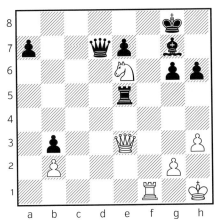

# (22)

▷ **K. Kulaots**
► **M. Agopov**
Finnland, 2016.03.12

1. +-

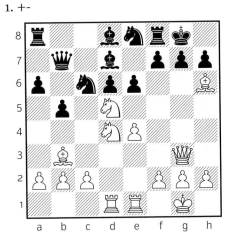

# (23)

▷ **Wang Hao**
► **Nguyen Ahn Dung**
HD Bank Cup, 2016.03.13

1. +-

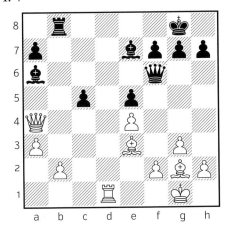

# (24)

▷ **H. Melkumyan**
► **D. Di Bernardino**
Reykjavik Open, 2016.03.16

1. +-

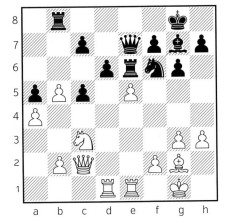

## (25)

▷ **V. Bernadskiy**
► **V. Borisenko**
Lviv rapid, 2016.03.16

1. +-

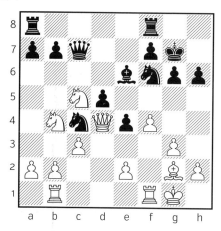

## (26)

▷ **S. Shankland**
► **J. Haug**
Fagernes Open, 2016.03.20

1. +-

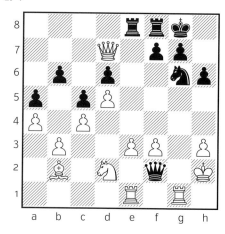

## (27)

▷ **K. Grigoryan**
► **D. Roldan Marques**
Paz de Ziganda rapid, 2016.03.20

1. +-

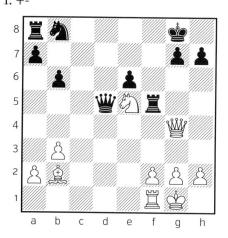

## (28)

▷ **H. Melkumyan**
► **T. Boyd**
Doeberl Cup, 2016.03.25

1. +-

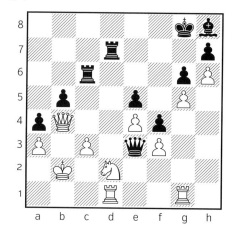

## (29)

▷ **S. Karjakin**
► **F. Caruana**
Candidates, 2016.03.28

1. +-

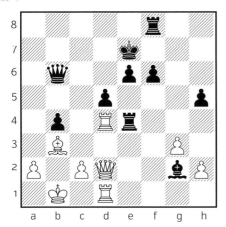

## (30)

▷ **A. Saric**
► **R. Berzinsh**
Karpos Open, 2016.04.02

1... -+

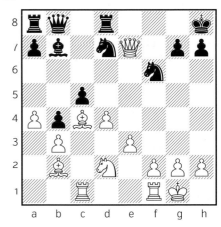

## (31)

▷ **A. Stukopin**
► **K. Griffith**
us College Final Four, 2016.04.03

1. +-

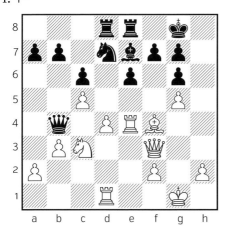

## (32)

▷ **A. Saric**
► **S. Tsolakidou**
Karpos Open, 2016.04.03

1... =

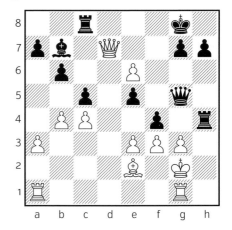

## (33)

▷ **K. Piorun**
► **M. Bartel**
Polish Championship, 2016.04.04

1... =

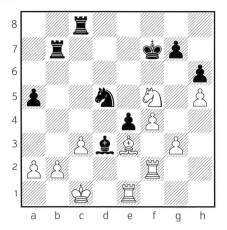

## (34)

▷ **Z. Kozul**
► **M. Percivaldi**
Karpos Open, 2016.04.04

1. +-

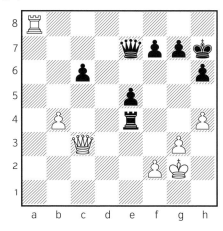

## (35)

▷ **B. Adhiban**
► **M. Dzhumaev**
Asian Nations Cup, 2016.04.04

1. +-

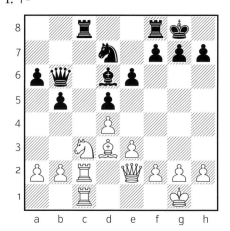

## (36)

▷ **S. Sethuraman**
► **Nguyen Huynh Minh**
Asian Nations Cup, 2016.04.05

1. +-

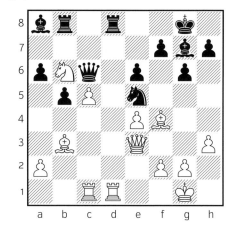

# (37)

▷ **R. Jumabayev**
► **B. Gundavaa**
Asian Nations Cup, 2016.04.05

1.. +-

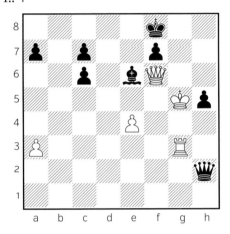

# (38)

▷ **A. David**
► **A. Petrisor**
Romanian Championship, 2016.04.05

1. +-

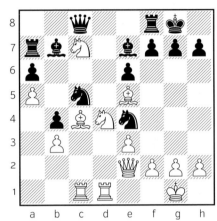

# (39)

▷ **I. Sokolov**
► **S. Das**
Dubai Open, 2016.04.12

1. +-

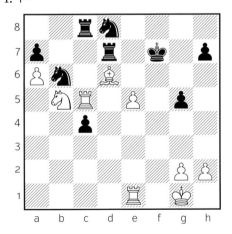

# (40)

▷ **A. Chandra**
► **W. So**
US Championship, 2016.04.15

1. +-

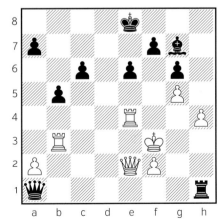

## (41)

▷ **W. So**
▶ **V. Akobian**
US Championship, 2016.04.18

1. +−

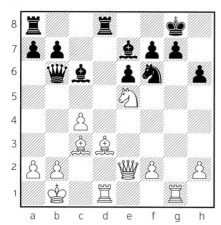

## (42)

▷ **F. Caruana**
▶ **A. Onischuk**
US Championship, 2016.04.20

1. +−

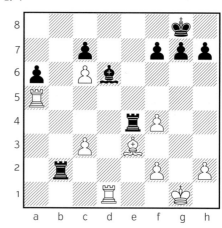

## (43)

▷ **A. Shabalov**
▶ **W. So**
US Championship, 2016.04.21

1... −+

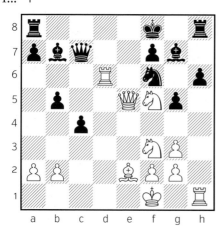

## (44)

▷ **T. Vandenbussche**
▶ **T. Henrichs**
Dutch league, 2016.04.23

1. +−

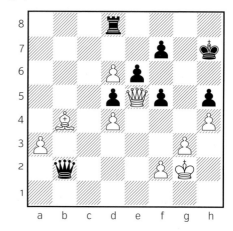

# (45)

▷ **Wei Yi**
► **Wang Chen**
Chinese Championship, 2016.04.24

1. +-

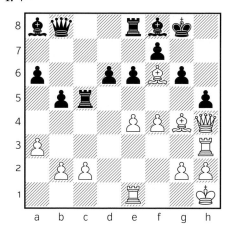

# (46)

▷ **J. Van Foreest**
► **H. Groffen**
Dutch league, 2016.04.24

1. +-

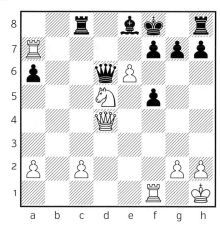

# (47)

▷ **V. Topalov**
► **A. Giri**
Norway Chess, 2016.04.27

1... =

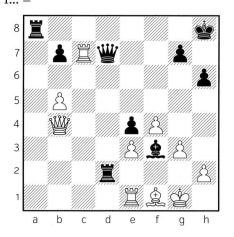

# (48)

▷ **W. So**
► **H. Nakamura**
Ultimate Chess Challenge, 2016.04.28

1. +-

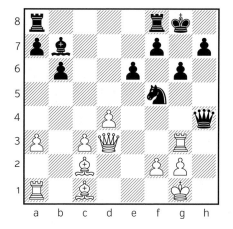

# (49)

▷ **A. Bachmann**
► **J. Lundvik**
Hasselbacken Open, 2016.05.01

1. +−

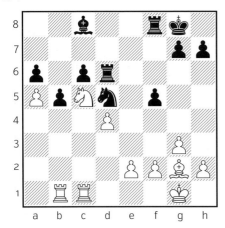

# (50)

▷ **A. Shirov**
► **R. Akesson**
Hasselbacken Open, 2016.05.02

1. +−

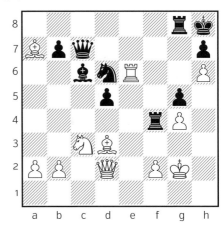

# (51)

▷ **D. Dubov**
► **A. Korobov**
Russian league, 2016.05.02

1. +−

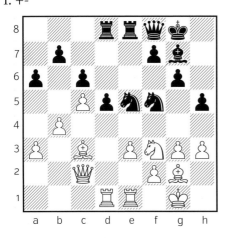

# (52)

▷ **N. Vitiugov**
► **E. Tomashevsky**
Russian league, 2016.05.04

1... −+

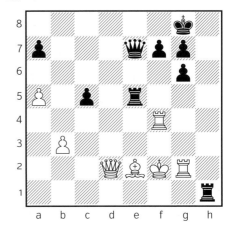

# (53)

▷ **L. Dominguez Perez**
▶ **I. Nepomniachtchi**
Russian league, 2016.05.06

1... -+

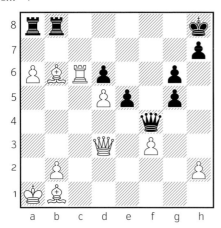

# (54)

▷ **A. Sharafiev**
▶ **V. Zvjagintsev**
Russian league, 2016.05.08

1... -+

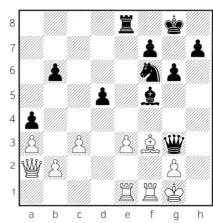

# (55)

▷ **E. Najer**
▶ **E. Timofeev**
Russian league, 2016.05.08

1. +-

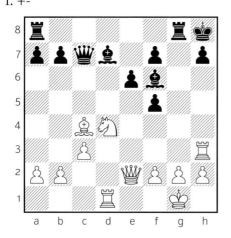

# (56)

▷ **I. Cheparinov**
▶ **U. Atakisi**
European Championship, 2016.05.12

1. +-

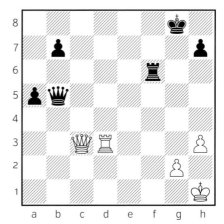

# (57)

▷ **M. Petrosyan**
► **H. Gabuzyan**
European Championship, 2016.05.13

1. +-

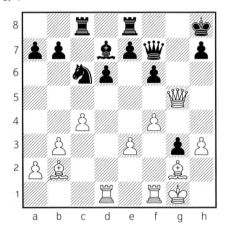

# (58)

▷ **R. Edouard**
► **T. Stremavicius**
Llucmajor Open, 2016.05.14

1. +-

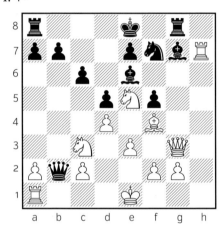

# (59)

▷ **V. Asadli**
► **Y. Kuzubov**
Nakhchivan Open, 2016.05.14

1... -+

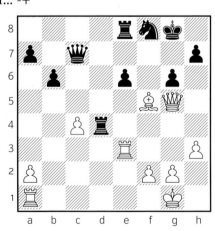

# (60)

▷ **D. Navara**
► **Z. Sturua**
European Championship, 2016.05.15

1. +-

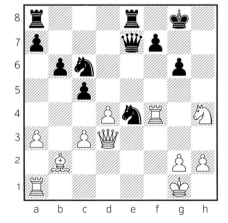

## (61)

▷ **D. Nisipeanu**
► **D. Khismatullin**
European Championship, 2016.05.22

1. +/-

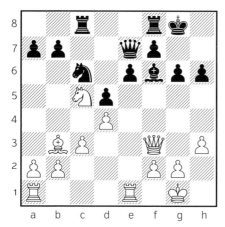

## (62)

▷ **D. Khismatullin**
► **D. Yudin**
Kurnosov memorial, 2016.05.26

1. +-

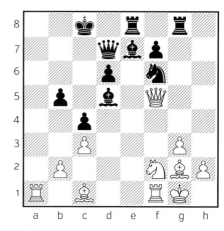

## (63)

▷ **R. Shcherbakov**
► **V. Gunina**
Kurnosov memorial, 2016.05.27

1. +-

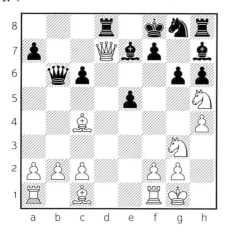

## (64)

▷ **P. Potapov**
► **P. Maletin**
Kurnosov memorial, 2016.05.27

1... -+

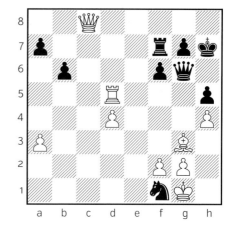

# (65)

▷ **Le Quang Liem**
▶ **M. Kazhgaleyev**
Asian Continental, 2016.05.28

1. +-

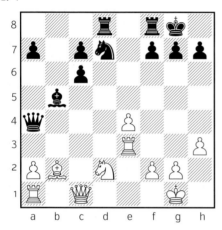

# (66)

▷ **R. Kasimdzhanov**
▶ **B. Lalith**
Asian Continental, 2016.05.29

1... =

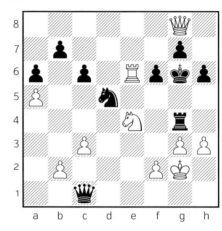

# (67)

▷ **M. Kravtsiv**
▶ **G. Szabo**
Zalakaros Open, 2016.06.04

1. +-

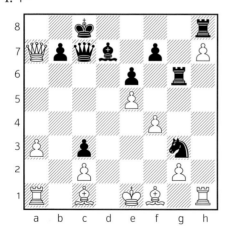

# (68)

▷ **L. Fressinet**
▶ **M. Carlsen**
Grand tour, Paris rapid, 2016.06.10

1... -+

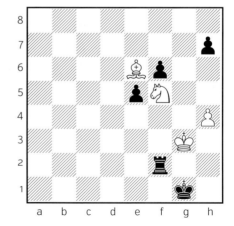

## (69)

▷ **M. Vachier Lagrave**
▶ **V. Anand**
GCT Rapid, 2016.06.17

1... -+

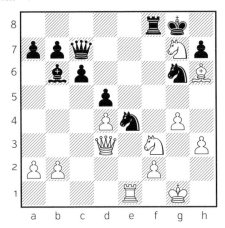

## (70)

▷ **D. Navara**
▶ **M. Bartel**
Lublin, 2016.06.17

1. +-

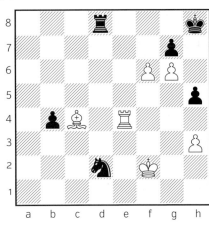

## (71)

▷ **J. Tomczak**
▶ **D. Navara**
Lublin, 2016.06.18

1... -+

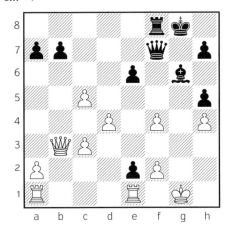

## (72)

▷ **A. Shirov**
▶ **R. Wang**
Edmonton, 2016.06.18

1. +-

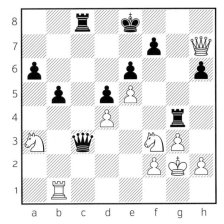

## (73)

▷ **D. Andreikin**
► **A. Volokitin**
Eurasian Blitz Champ., 2016.06.18

1. +-

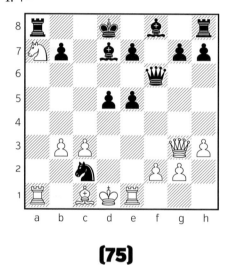

## (74)

▷ **W. So**
► **F. Caruana**
Grand tour, Leuven blitz, 2016.06.19

1. +-

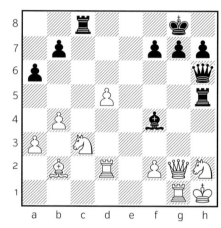

## (75)

▷ **V. Moiseenko**
► **E. Romanov**
Russian Higher league, 2016.06.22

1... -+

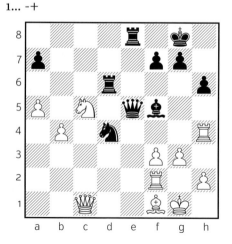

## (76)

▷ **R. Wojtaszek**
► **B. Heberla**
Polish league, 2016.06.24

1. +-

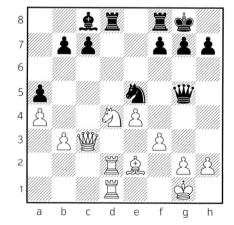

# (77)

▷ **Wen Yang**
► **E. Inarkiev**
Chinese league, 2016.06.25

1... -+

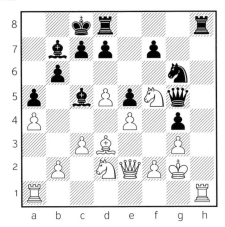

# (78)

▷ **A. Naiditsch**
► **J. Borisek**
Vidmar memorial, 2016.06.27

1. +/-

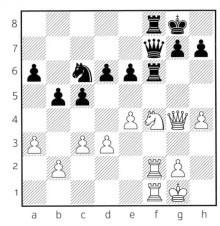

# (79)

▷ **Z. Kozul**
► **A. Beliavsky**
Vidmar memorial, 2016.06.28

1. +-

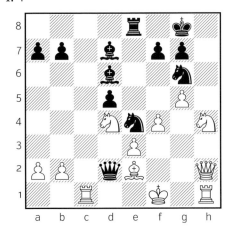

# (80)

▷ **A. Gabrielian**
► **A. Esipenko**
Russian Higher league, 2016.06.29

1. +-

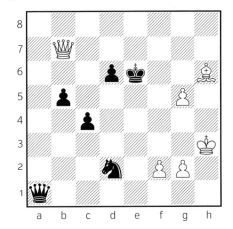

# (81)

▷ **A. Areshchenko**
► **N. Grandelius**
Porticcio Open, 2016.06.29

1. +−

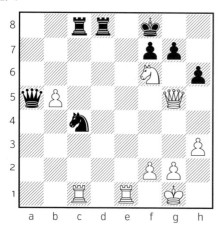

# (82)

▷ **S. Bilguun**
► **K. Dragun**
Najdorf memorial, 2016.07.12

1. +−

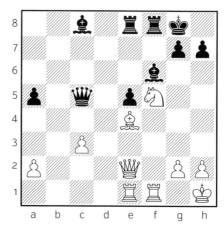

# (83)

▷ **S. Fedorchuk**
► **J. Moussard**
Paris, 2016.07.16

1... −+

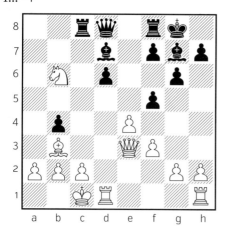

# (84)

▷ **S. Fedorchuk**
► **J. Moussard**
Paris, 2016.07.16

1... −+

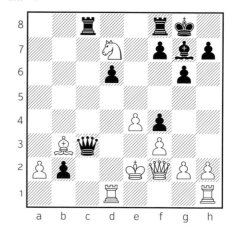

## (85)

▷ **A. Firouzja**
▶ **A. Dreev**
Stars Cup, 2016.07.18

1... -+

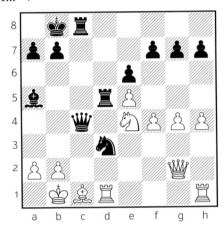

## (86)

▷ **Ding Liren**
▶ **A. Grischuk**
Wenzhou match, 2016.07.21

1. +-

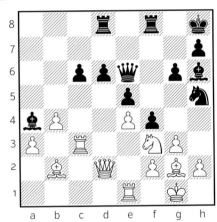

## (87)

▷ **V. Bologan**
▶ **A. Korobov**
Poikovsky, 2016.07.24

1. +-

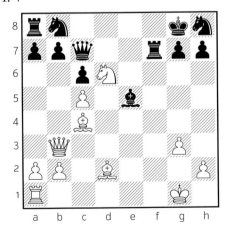

## (88)

▷ **E. Zanan**
▶ **V. Laznicka**
Pardubice, 2016.07.25

1... -+

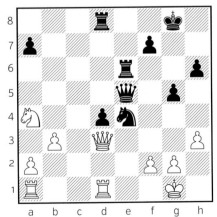

# (89)

▷ **Wang Chen**
► **Ding Liren**
Chinese league, 2016.07.25

1. +−

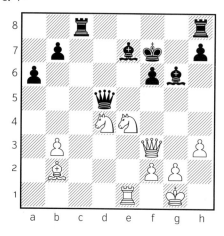

# (90)

▷ **R. Mamedov**
► **E. Demircioglu**
Turkish league, 2016.07.25

1. +−

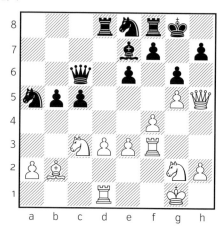

# (91)

▷ **N. Georgiadis**
► **B. Bok**
Biel, 2016.07.26

1... −+

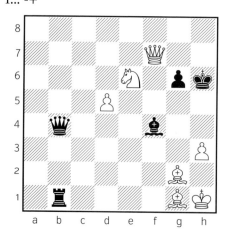

# (92)

▷ **B. Amin**
► **E. Zude**
Xtracon Open, 2016.07.27

1. +−

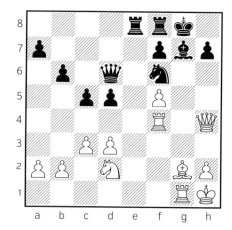

# (93)

▷ **A. Shirov**
► **J. Timman**
Xtracon Open, 2016.07.29

1. +−

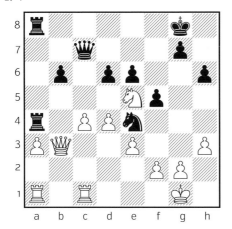

# (94)

▷ **A. Donchenko**
► **M. Bartel**
Biel Open, 2016.07.29

1... −+

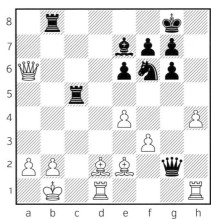

# (95)

▷ **D. Jakovenko**
► **V. Bologan**
Poikovsky, 2016.07.30

1. +−

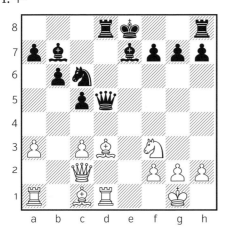

# (96)

▷ **R. Panjwani**
► **L. Bruzon**
Calgary Open, 2016.07.31

1. +−

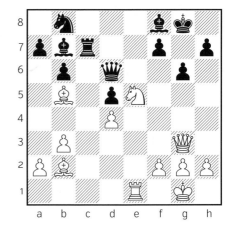

# (97)

▷ **S. Mamedyarov**
▶ **B. Savchenko**
Turkish league, 2016.08.02

1. +-

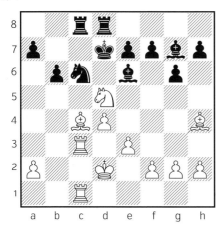

# (98)

▷ **V. Topalov**
▶ **P. Svidler**
Sinquefield Cup, 2016.08.05

1. +-

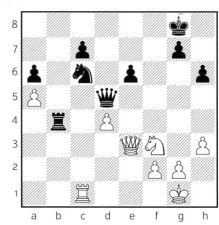

# (99)

▷ **E. Cordova**
▶ **J. Sylvan**
Badalona Open, 2016.08.07

1. +-

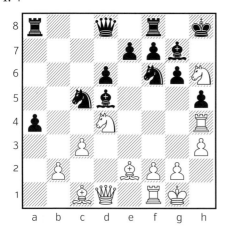

# (100)

▷ **H. Nakamura**
▶ **Ding Liren**
Sinquefield Cup, 2016.08.14

1. +-

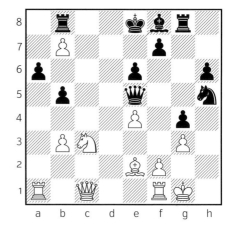

## (101)

▷ F. Olivares
► K. Sasikiran
Sants Open, 2016.08.21

1. +−

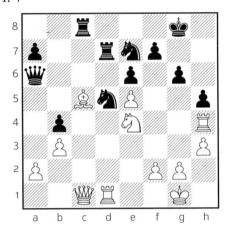

## (102)

▷ D. Sadzikowski
► T. Banusz
Abu Dhabi Open, 2016.08.23

1. +−

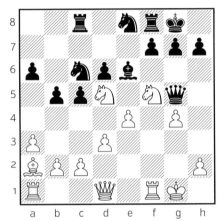

## (103)

▷ F. Perez Ponsa
► N. Georgiadis
Olympiad, 2016.09.03

1. +−

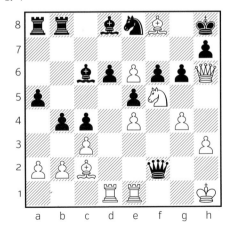

## (104)

▷ A. Bachmann
► J. Gomez
Olympiad, 2016.09.03

1. +−

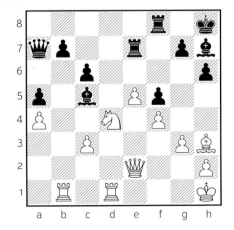

# (105)

▷ **K. Piorun**
► **L. Draskovic**
Olympiad, 2016.09.05

1. +-

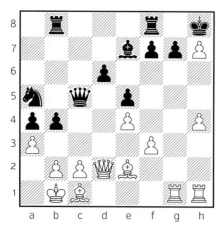

# (106)

▷ **C. Lupulescu**
► **S. Mamedyarov**
Olympiad, 2016.09.05

1... -/+

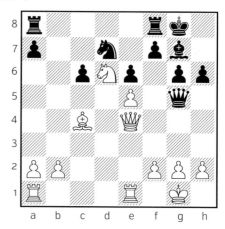

# (107)

▷ **A. Shirov**
► **R. Rapport**
Olympiad, 2016.09.06

1. +-

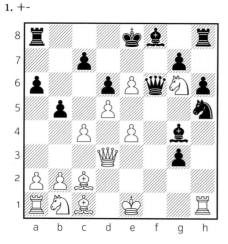

# (108)

▷ **Wang Yue**
► **S. Mareco**
Olympiad, 2016.09.08

1... -+

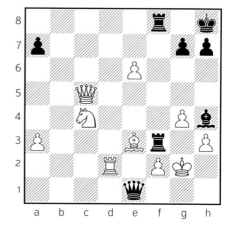

## (109)

▷ **Li Chao**
▶ **Z. Almasi**
Olympiad, 2016.09.10

1... -+

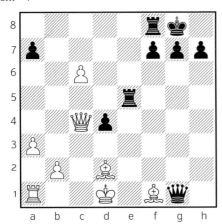

## (110)

▷ **B. Jobava**
▶ **R. Ponomariov**
Olympiad, 2016.09.10

1. +-

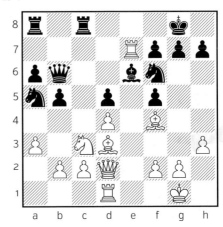

## (111)

▷ **J. Gomez**
▶ **F. Perez Ponsa**
Olympiad, 2016.09.11

1... -+

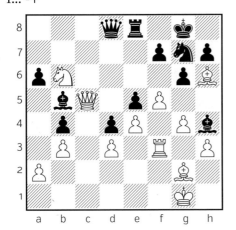

## (112)

▷ **D. Nisipeanu**
▶ **A. Volodin**
Olympiad, 2016.09.13

1. +-

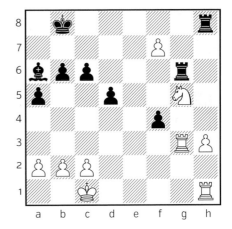

## (113)

▷ N. Tutisani
► L. Pantsulaia
Georgian league, 2016.09.22

1... -+

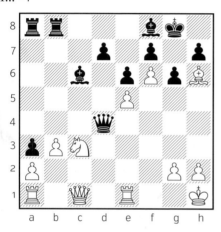

## (114)

▷ M. Parligras
► D. Solak
Serbian league, 2016.09.22

1... -+

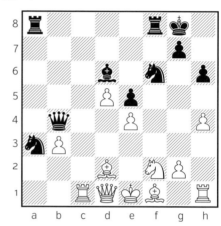

## (115)

▷ Zhang Zhong
► X. Xu
Chinese league, 2016.09.24

1. +-

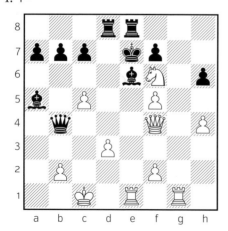

## (116)

▷ L. Van Wely
► E. Iturrizaga
Spanish league, 2016.09.26

1. +-

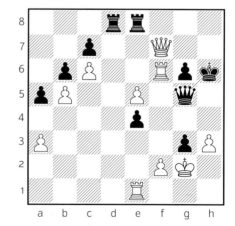

# (117)

▷ **D. Anton Guijjaro**
► **T. Banusz**
Spanish league, 2016.09.26

1. +−

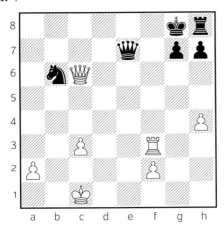

# (118)

▷ **A. Naiditsch**
► **A. Gupta**
Isle of Man, 2016.10.04

1. +−

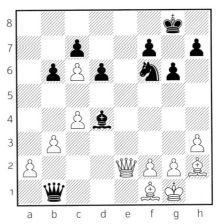

# (119)

▷ **J. Granda Zuniga**
► **W. So**
Isle of Man, 2016.10.04

1... −+

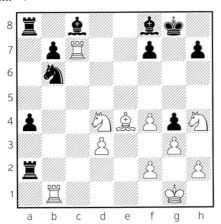

# (120)

▷ **S. Tiviakov**
► **T. Kotanjian**
Yerevan Open, 2016.10.10

1. +−

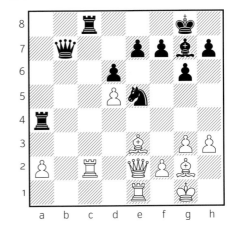

## (121)

▷ **A. Markgraf**
► **A. Braun**
German league, 2016.10.16

1... -+

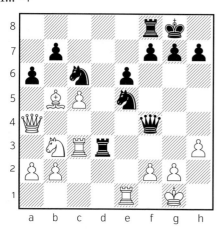

## (122)

▷ **K. Sychev**
► **B. Savchenko**
Moscow league, 2016.10.23

1. +-

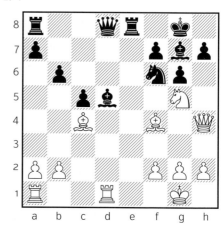

## (123)

▷ **A. Moiseenko**
► **T. Radjabov**
Corsican Circuit, 2016.10.28

1... -+

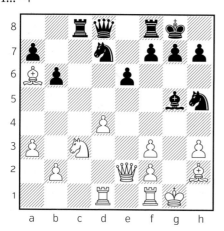

## (124)

▷ **V. Zvjagintsev**
► **D. Schwarz**
European Club Cup, 2016.11.06

1. +-

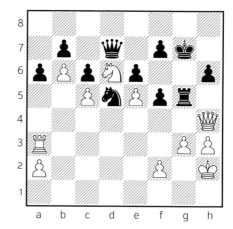

## (125)

▷ E. Blomqvist
► C. Noe
European Club Cup, 2016.11.06

1... -+

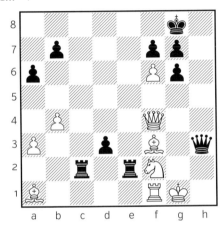

## (126)

▷ P. Harikrishna
► M. Bluebaum
European Club Cup, 2016.11.09

1. +-

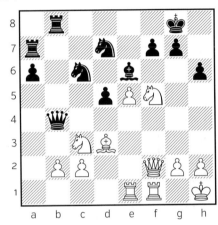

## (127)

▷ V. Fedoseev
► M. Perunovic
European Club Cup, 2016.11.09

1. +-

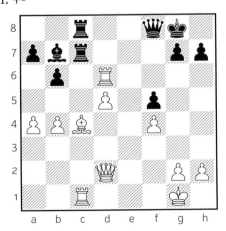

## (128)

▷ L. Dominguez Perez
► D. Andreikin
European Club Cup, 2016.11.10

1... -/+

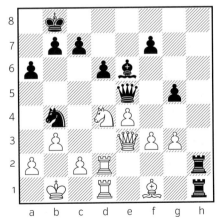

## (129)

▷ F. Caruana
► H. Nakamura
Champions Showdown Rapid, 2016.11.10

1. +/-

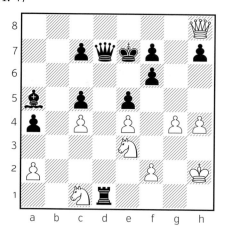

## (130)

▷ H. Nakamura
► V. Topalov
Champions Showdown Rapid, 2016.11.11

1. +-

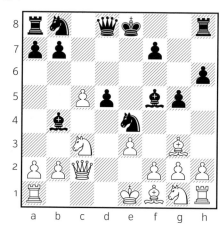

## (131)

▷ V. Mikhalevski
► Bu Xiangzhi
European Club Cup, 2016.11.11

1... -+

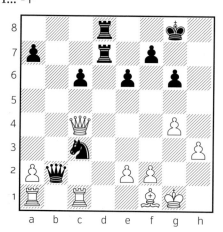

## (132)

▷ V. Topalov
► H. Nakamura
Champions Showdown, 2016.11.12

1. +-

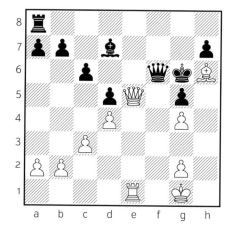

## (133)

▷ **F. Caruana**
► **V. Topalov**
Champions Showdown Blitz, 2016.11.14

1. +-

## (134)

▷ **A. Chandra**
► **B. Finegold**
Saint Louis, 2016.11.18

1. +-

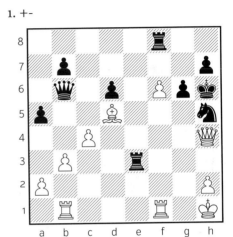

## (135)

▷ **J. Sriram**
► **M. Karthikeyan**
Indian Championship, 2016.11.24

1... -+

## (136)

▷ **J. Glud**
► **H. Ziska**
Runavik Open, 2016.11.24

1... -+

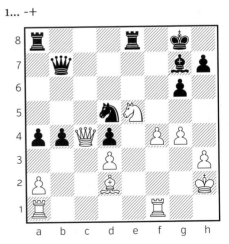

## (137)

▷ V. Fedoseev
► A. Goganov
Governor's Cup, 2016.11.24

1. +-

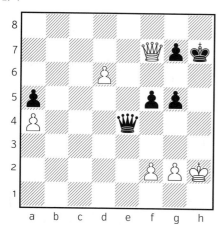

## (138)

▷ J. Radlovacki
► M. Savic
Belgrade Open, 2016.11.26

1. +-

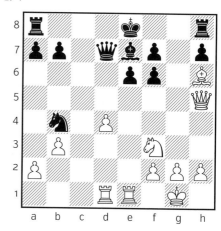

## (139)

▷ V. Hamitevici
► H. Ziska
Runavik Open, 2016.11.26

1... -+

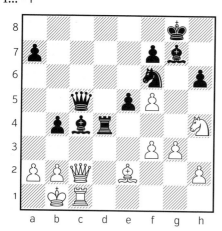

## (140)

▷ C. Foisor
► L. Vajda
Kings Rapid RR, 2016.11.29

1. +-

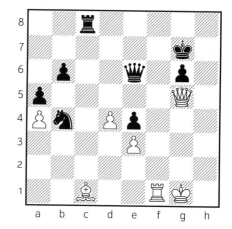

# (141)

▷ I. Lysyj
► M. Demidov
Russian Rapid Cup, 2016.12.03

1. +-

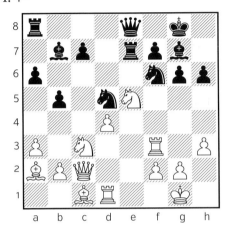

# (142)

▷ M. Vachier Lagrave
► J. Krassowizkij
German league, 2016.12.04

1. +-

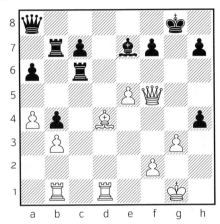

# (143)

▷ S. Sjugirov
► S. Yudin
Russian Cup, 2016.12.06

1. +-

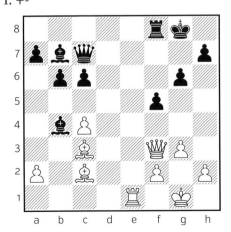

# (144)

▷ V. Topalov
► F. Caruana
London, 2016.12.10

1... -+

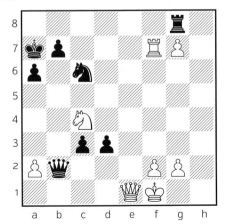

# (145)

▷ **K. Arkell**
► **S. Maze**
London Open, 2016.12.11

1. +-

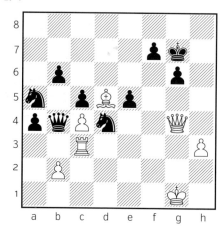

# (146)

▷ **D. Martins**
► **A. Gupta**
London Open, 2016.12.12

1... -+

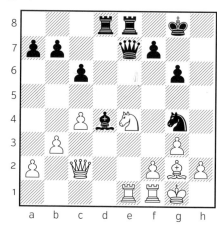

# – SOLUTIONS –

## (1)

▷ M. Rodshtein (2678)
► A. Donchenko (2588)
Rilton Cup, 04.01.2016

**12.♕a4!!** [12.♘c3? ♖b8 13.♕a4 ♖b4] **12...♗xf3** [12...f5 13.d3!+-; 12...♗d5 13.♘c3+-] **13.♗xf3 0-0 14.♗xc6+-**

## (2)

▷ S. Mamedyarov (2747)
► L. Van Wely (2640)
Wijk aan Zee A, 16.01.2016

**17...♕xb5?** [17...♘g4! 18.fxe3 (18. ♖xa7 ♗xf2+ 19.♔h1 ♕c6+-+) 18... ♕xe3+ 19.♔g2 (19.♔h1 ♕e4+! 20.♖f3 ♘f2+-+) 19...♕e4+! 20.♖f3 (20.♔g1 ♘e3-+) 20...♘e3+-+] **18.fxe3∓**

## (3)

▷ I. Popov (2650)
► M. Kunal (2390)
Chennai Open, 20.01.2016

**19.♘xf7!!** ♖xe1+ [19...♔xf7 20.♕f3+ ♔g8 21.♕xd5+ ♔h7 22.♕xa5+-] **20.♖xe1 ♔xf7 21.♕f3+ ♔g8 22.♕xd5+ ♔h7 23.♕xa5+-**

## (4)

▷ D. Nisipeanu (2679)
► A. Haast (2391)
Wijk aan Zee B, 23.01.2016

**15...♘xh3+! 16.♔f1** [16.gxh3 ♗xf2+!! 17.♘xf2 ♕g3+ 18.♔f1 (18.♔h1 ♘xf3-+) 18...♗xh3+ 19.♘xh3 ♕xh3+ 20.♔f2 ♘g4+-+] **16...♘xf3 17.♕xf3 ♗g4 18.♕g3 ♕xg3 19.fxg3 ♖ae8!**

## 

**20.♗d2** [20.gxh3 ♗xh3+ 21.♔e2 ♖xe4+-+] **20...♔h8-+** [20...♖e5-+]

## (5)

▷ A. Tukhaev (2556)
► C. Deepan (2478)
Chennai Open, 25.01.2016

**29.♖g5! ♕e6** [29...♕d7 30.♖e5+ ♔d8 31.♗g5++-] **30.♖e5! 1-0** [30. ♖e5 ♕xe5 31.♕xc8+ ♔e7 32.♗c5+! ♔f6 33.♕xh8+ ♔e6 34.♕xe5+ ♔xe5 35.♔xd1+-]

## (6)

▷ J. Van Foreest (2541)
► B. Bok (2607)
Wijk aan Zee B, 27.01.2016

**29.♖xg7! ♔xg7 30.♖g1+ ♔f6** [30... ♔h8 31.♖g5! ♕h6 32.♖g8+! ♖xg8 33.♕xh6+-] **31.♖g5 ♕h6 32.e5++-**

## (7)

▷ N. Short (2684)
► D. Harika (2511)
Gibraltar Open, 28.01.2016

**30...♕xd5! 31.♕xd5 ♗c2!! 0-1** [31... exd5? 32.♗xf5; 31...♗c2 32.♕xc6 (32. ♗b2 exd5-+) 32...♖b1#]

## (8)

▷ M. Muzychuk (2554)
► R. Rapport (2721)
Gibraltar Open, 02.02.2016

**25...♖xc4!! 26.bxc4 ♗a4-+ 27.♖xe6+ ♕xe6 28.♘f5+ ♔f8 29.♖d8+ ♗e8-+**

## (9)

▷ S. Vidit (2642)
► A. Pichot (2517)
Gibraltar Open, 03.02.2016

**34.h4+!** ♔xh4 [34...♔g6 35.♖e6+
♔g7 36.♕c3++-] **35.♘f6!!** ♖xf6
**36.♖e4+** 1–0 [36.♖e4+ ♔g5 37.♖g1+
♔h6 38.♕e3+ ♘f4 39.♖xf4+-]

## (10)

▷ A. Shirov (2684)
► H. Nakamura (2787)
Zurich, 13.02.2016

**38...h2!** 0–1 [38...h2 39.♔xh2 (39.♕c1
♕h8! 40.♕h1 ♕xe5–+) 39...♕h6+!
40.♔g3 ♖xg4+!–+]

## (11)

▷ G. Sarakauskas (2415)
► D. Howell (2693)
4NCL, 14.02.2016

**32...♘c3!!** **33.♔f3** [33.bxc3 ♗d5+
34.♔h2 ♖h1#; 33.♖xe3 ♗d5+ 34.♔f2
♖xb2+–+] **33...♘xe2–+**

## (12)

▷ E. Postny (2668)
► P. Schreiner (2435)
Graz Open, 15.02.2016

**36.♘d6!!** ♕d4+ [36...♕xd6
37.♕xh7#] **37.♔f1** ♘ef6 **38.♘xf7+**
♔g8 **39.♘g5+-** ♘f8 [39...♕xc3
40.♗xh7++-] **40.♕xf8+!** 1–0
[40.♕xf8+ ♔xf8 41.♘e6+ ♔e7
42.♘xd4+-]

## (13)

▷ L. Aronian (2792)
► V. Kramnik (2801)
Zurich blitz, 15.02.2016

**19.b5?** [19.♕c2!! ♗xd7 (19...♘xd7
20.♘g5 g6 21.♗xc6+-) 20.♗xf6 ♖c8
(20...gxf6 21.♘g5! fxg5 22.♗xa8+-)
21.♗c3 ♕c6 22.♘e4+-] **19...♗xd7**
**20.♗xf6 gxf6 21.♕g4+ ♔h8 22.♕d4**
**♕d5 23.♕xf6+ ♔g8∞**

## (14)

▷ D. Harika (2511)
► A. Stefanova (2509)
Tehran WGP, 16.02.2016

**26.♘f6!** ♔c8 [26...♗xf6 27.gxf6
♖xf6 28.♖d5 (28.♗g5+-) 28...♖fe6
29.♖e1+-] **27.♗xe5 ♖xe5 28.♘d7** 1–0

## (15)

▷ R. Wojtaszek (2727)
► V. Ivanchuk (2710)
IMSA rapid, 26.02.2016

**11.♘b6!!** ♗e6 [11...♕xd1+ 12.♖xd1
axb6 13.♖d8#] **12.♘xa8+-**

## (16)

▷ R. Wojtaszek (2727)
► P. Harikrishna (2753)
IMSA blitz, 29.02.2016

**22.♘xf7!** ♔xf7 **23.♖e6?** [23.♖e7+!
♔f8 (23...♕xe7 24.d6++-) 24.♖xb7+-]
**23...♖e8!!∞**

## (17)

▷ R. Ponomariov (2712)
► Wang Yue (2718)
IMSA blitz, 29.02.2016

14.♗xh6!! gxh6 15.♖xe6! fxe6
16.♕g6+ ♔h8 17.♕xh6+ ♔g8
18.♕g6+ ♔h8 19.♘g5!+− ♖xf1+
20.♔xf1 ♕f8+ 21.♘f7+ 1−0

## (18)

▷ Li Chao (2751)
► Wang Hao (2717)
IMSA blitz, 29.02.2016

27.♕xc4!! ♘xc4 28.♖e8+ ♔g7
29.♗f8+ 1−0 [29.♗f8+ ♔g6 (29...
♔g8 30.♗h6#) 30.♗e4+!+−]

## (19)

▷ Hou Yifan (2673)
► M. Muzychuk (2554)
World Championship, 03.03.2016

29.♖xd5! ♗xf2 [29...cxd5 30.♖xf6
♖xf6 31.♕g5+−] 30.♗b3! ♘e6
31.♖d6+−

## (20)

▷ Hou Yifan (2673)
► M. Muzychuk (2554)
World Championship, 06.03.2016

18...♗c5!! 19.♕xc5 ♖h1+! 20.♔g2
♖h2+! 21.♔g1! [21.♔xh2? ♕h4+
22.♔g2 ♕h3+ 23.♔g1 ♕h1#] 21...
♖h1+= 1/2

## (21)

▷ V. Artemiev (2674)
► T. Petrosian (2607)
Aeroflot Open, 08.03.2016

30.♕xe5!! ♗xe5 31.♖f8+ ♔h7
32.♖f7+ ♗g7 33.♖xg7+ ♔h8
34.♖h7+!! ♔g8 [34...♔xh7? 35.♘f8+]
35.♖g7+ ♔h8 36.♖h7+ 1/2

## (22)

▷ K. Kulaots (2566)
► M. Agopov (2455)
Finnland, 12.03.2016

16.♘f5!! exf5 17.exf5 ♗xf5 18.♖xe8!
♗g6 [18...♖xe8 19.♕xg7#] 19.♖xf8+
♔xf8 20.♕xd6++−

## (23)

▷ Wang Hao (2717)
► Nguyen Ahn Dung (2478)
HD Bank Cup, 13.03.2016

21.♗f1! ♗xf1 22.♕xa7 ♖xb2 [22...
♖e8 23.♖xf1+−] 23.♕a8+! ♗f8
24.♗xc5 1−0

## (24)

▷ H. Melkumyan (2653)
► D. Di Bernardino (2511)
Reykjavik Open, 16.03.2016

20.exf6! ♖xe1+ 21.♔h2! ♗xf6
[21...♕e6 22.fxg7+−] 22.♘d5! ♕e2
23.♘xf6+ ♔g7 24.♖d2! 1−0

## [25]

▷ V. Bernadskiy (2526)
► V. Borisenko (2284)
Lviv rapid, 16.03.2016

**20.f5! gxf5** [20...♗xf5 21.♘xd5+-]
**21.♘xd5!! ♕e5** [21...♗xd5 22.♖xf5
♕d6 23.♖bf1+-] **22.♘xf6** [22.♕xe5
♘xe5 23.♘xf6 ♔xf6 24.♗xe4+-]
**22...♕xf6?** [22...♕xd4+ 23.cxd4
♔xf6 24.♗xe4±] **23.♘xe6+ fxe6
24.♕xc4+-**

## [26]

▷ S. Shankland (2648)
► J. Haug (2267)
Fagernes Open, 20.03.2016

**32.♖g2! ♕xe1 33.♖xg6! ♕xd2+** [33...
fxg6 34.♕xg7#] **34.♖g2! ♕xg2+
35.♔xg2+-**

## [27]

▷ K. Grigoryan (2612)
► D. Roldan Marques (2168)
Paz de Ziganda rapid, 20.03.2016

**23.♖d1! ♖xe5 24.f4!! ♕c5+ 25.♗d4!
♖e1+ 26.♔f2! ♕e7 27.♖xe1+-**

## [28]

▷ H. Melkumyan (2653)
► T. Boyd (2260)
Doeberl Cup, 25.03.2016

**35.♘b1!! ♕e2+ 36.♔a1! ♖xd1
37.♖xd1 ♕xd1 38.♕e7! ♕d6
39.♕e8+ ♕f8 40.♕xc6+-**

## [29]

▷ S. Karjakin (2760)
► F. Caruana (2794)
Candidates, 28.03.2016

**37.♖xd5! exd5 38.♕xd5 ♕c7** [38...
f5 39.♕d7+ ♔f6 40.♖d6+ ♕xd6
41.♕xd6++-; 38...♖d4 39.♕xd4
♕xd4 40.♖xd4+-] **39.♕f5! ♖f7** [39...
♕c6 40.♕h7+ ♔e8 41.♕xh5+ ♔e7
42.♗d5+-] **40.♗xf7+-**

## [30]

▷ A. Saric (2594)
► R. Berzinsh (2394)
Karpos Open, 02.04.2016

**17...♖e8! 18.♕xf7 ♕d8!! 19.e4** [19.dxc5
♖e7 20.♗xf6 ♘xf6-+] **19...♖e7-+**

## [31]

▷ A. Stukopin (2578)
► K. Griffith (2284)
US College Final Four, 03.04.2016

**20.♗c7! ♖c8 21.d5! ♕xc5 22.b4!+-**

## [32]

▷ A. Saric (2594)
► S. Tsolakidou (2355)
Karpos Open, 03.04.2016

**22...♗xf3+?** [22...♕xg3+! 23.♔f1
♖h1! 24.♖xh1 fxe3 25.♕f7+! ♔h8
26.♖xh7+! ♔xh7 27.♕h5+ ♔g8
28.♕f7+=] **23.♔xf3+-**

## [33]

▷ K. Piorun (2655)
► M. Bartel (2625)
Polish Championship, 04.04.2016

41...♖xc3+! 42.bxc3 ♖b1+ 43.♔d2 ♖b2+ 44.♔d1 ♘xe3+! 45.♖xe3 [45. ♘xe3 ♖xf2=] 45...♖b1+=

## [34]

▷ Z. Kozul (2609)
► M. Percivaldi (2270)
Karpos Open, 04.04.2016

35.♕f3! ♖xb4 36.♕f5+ 1–0 [36.♕f5+ g6 37.♕c8+-]

## [35]

▷ B. Adhiban (2663)
► M. Dzhumaev (2481)
Asian Nations Cup, 04.04.2016

20.♘xd5! ♖xc2 21.♗xh7+!! 1–0 [21. ♗xh7+ ♔h8 (21...♔xh7 22.♕xc2+ ♔g8 23.♘xb6+-) 22.♗xc2 exd5 23.♕h5+ ♔g8 24.♕h7#]

## [36]

▷ S. Sethuraman (2658)
► Nguyen Huynh Minh (2455)
Asian Nations Cup, 05.04.2016

25.♗d5!! exd5 26.exd5 ♕e8 [26...♕f6 27.♗g5 ♕f5 28.♗xd8 ♖xd8 29.c6+-] 27.c6!+-

## [37]

▷ R. Jumabayev (2607)
► B. Gundavaa (2517)
Asian Nations Cup, 05.04.2016

55.♔h6!! ♕d2+ [55...♕xg3 56.♕d8#] 56.♔h7 ♗g4 57.♖b3 1–0

## [38]

▷ A. David (2365)
► A. Petrisor (2412)
Romanian Championship,
05.04.2016

21.♘cxe6!! fxe6 22.♗xe6+! ♘xe6 23.♖xc8 ♗xc8 24.♕c4! ♘4c5 25.♘c6! ♖d7 26.♘xe7+ [26.♖xd7 ♗xd7 27.♘xe7++-] 26...♖xe7 27.♗d6 ♖d8 28.♖d4+-

## [39]

▷ I. Sokolov (2626)
► S. Das (2435)
Dubai Open, 12.04.2016

34.e6+! ♘xe6 35.♖f5+! ♔g6 36.♖xe6+! 1–0 [36.♖xe6+ ♔xf5 37.♘d4+ ♔g4 38.h3+ ♔h5 39.g4+ ♔h4 40.♖h6#]

## [40]

▷ A. Chandra (2477)
► W. So (2773)
US Championship, 15.04.2016

33.♔g4? [33.♖xe6+! fxe6 34.♕xe6+ ♔f8 (34...♔d8 35.♕d6+! ♔c8 36.♕xc6+ ♔d8 37.♕d6+ ♔c8 38.♕c5+ ♔d8 39.♖d3++-) 35.♖d3! ♗d4 36.♕d6+ ♔e8 (36...♔f7 37.♕d7+ ♔f8 38.♖xd4+-) 37.♕xg6+ ♔e7 38.♕e4+ ♔d6 39.♖xd4++-] 33...♔f8!∓

## [41]

▷ W. So (2773)
► V. Akobian (2615)
US Championship, 18.04.2016

20.♘xf7! ♔xf7 21.♖xg7+!! ♔xg7 22.♕xe6 ♕xf2 [22...♖e8 23.♕f5! (23.

♖g1+ ♔f8 24.♗xf6 ♗g2!!) 23...♔f8
24.♗d2!+-] **23.♕xe7+ ♔g8 24.♗h7+**
**1–0** [24.♗h7+ ♘xh7 25.♕g7#;
24.♗xf6+-]

## [42]

▷ **F. Caruana (2795)**
► **A. Onischuk (2664)**
us Championship, 20.04.2016

**25.♖e5!! ♖xe3** [25...♗xe5 26.♖d8#;
25...♖xe5 26.fxe5 ♗f8 27.♖d7+-; 25...f5
26.♖xe4 fxe4 27.♖xd6! cxd6 28.c7+-]
**26.fxe3+-**

## [43]

▷ **A. Shabalov (2528)**
► **W. So (2773)**
us Championship, 21.04.2016

**21...♘e8! 22.♘xg7 ♕xd6 23.♘e6+**
**♔g8! 0–1**

## [44]

▷ **T. Vandenbussche (2421)**
► **T. Henrichs (2464)**
Dutch league, 23.04.2016

**48.♕f6! ♖d7 49.♕e7!! ♖xe7**
**50.dxe7+-**

## [45]

▷ **Wei Yi (2700)**
► **Wang Chen (2514)**
Chinese Championship, 24.04.2016

**28.b4! 1–0** [28.b4 ♖xc2 29.♗xh5+-]

## [46]

▷ **J. Van Foreest (2541)**
► **H. Groffen (2152)**
Dutch league, 24.04.2016

**24.♘f6!! 1–0** [24.♘f6 ♕xd4 (24...
♕xe6 25.♕b4++-) 25.e7#]

## [47]

▷ **V. Topalov (2754)**
► **A. Giri (2790)**
Norway Chess, 27.04.2016

**37...♖xh2!! 38.♖xd7 ♖h1+ 39.♔f2**
**♖h2+ 40.♔g2 ♖xg2+ 41.♔f1 ♖h2!!=**
**42.♖d2 ♖h1+ 43.♔f2 1/2**

## [48]

▷ **W. So (2773)**
► **H. Nakamura (2787)**
Ultimate Chess Challenge (blitz),
28.04.2016

**19.♗g5! ♕h5 20.♗d1! ♘xg3**
**21.♕xg3! 1–0**

## [49]

▷ **A. Bachmann (2621)**
► **J. Lundvik (2204)**
Hasselbacken Open, 01.05.2016

**26.♘xa6! ♗xa6 27.♖xc6! ♖ff6**
**28.♖xa6! ♖xa6 29.♗xd5+ ♔f8**
**30.♖xb5 ♖a7 31.♗b7+- 1–0**

## [50]

▷ **A. Shirov (2686)**
► **R. Akesson (2452)**
Hasselbacken Open, 02.05.2016

30.♕xf4! d4+ [30...gxf4 31.♗d4+
♖g7 32.hxg7+ ♔g8 33.♖h6+-] 31.♔g1
gxf4 32.♗xd4+ ♖g7 33.hxg7+
♔g8 34.♖xd6 1-0 [34.♖xd6 ♕xd6
35.♗c4++-]

## (51)

▷ D. Dubov (2644)
► A. Korobov (2674)
Russian league, 02.05.2016

24.♗xe5! ♖xe5 [24...♗xe5 25.e4!
dxe4 (25...♘g7 26.exd5+-) 26.♖xd8
♖xd8 27.♘xe5+-] 25.♘xe5 ♗xe5
26.e4+-

## (52)

▷ N. Vitiugov (2721)
► E. Tomashevsky (2722)
Russian league, 04.05.2016

39...♖f5? [39...g5! 40.♖c4 (40.♖f3
g4! 41.♖f4 (41.♖xg4 ♖xe2+ 42.♕xe2
♖h2+-+) 41...♕h4+-+) 40...♕f6+
41.♗f3 ♖ee1-+] 40.♖xf5 ♕h4+
41.♔e3! gxf5 42.♗f3 ♕e7+ 43.♔f2
♕h4+ ½

## (53)

▷ L. Dominguez Perez (2732)
► I. Nepomniachtchi (2703)
Russian league, 06.05.2016

37...♕a4+! 38.♕a3 ♕xa6! 39.♗c7
♕b7! 40.♗xb8 ♖xa3+ 41.bxa3
♕xb8-+

## (54)

▷ A. Sharafiev (2435)
► V. Zvjagintsev (2672)
Russian league, 08.05.2016

27...♖e4! 28.b4 [28.♗xe4 ♘g4-+]
28...♖h4-+ 29.♖d1 ♘e4 30.♗xe4
♗xe4 31.♖f2 ♖h5! [31...♖h2
32.♖xd5!] 32.♕d2 [32.c4 ♕h4-+]
32...♖h2! 33.c4 ♕h4 0-1

## (55)

▷ E. Najer (2681)
► E. Timofeev (2598)
Russian league, 08.05.2016

20.♘xf5!! exf5 21.♖xh7+! ♔xh7
22.♕h5+ ♔g7 23.♕xf7+ ♔h6
24.♕xf6+ [24.♖xd7+-] 24...♖g6
25.♕h4+ ♔g7 26.♕e7+ ♔h6
27.♖xd7+- ♕xc4 28.♕h7+ [28.
♕e3++-] 28...♔g5 29.♖d4! 1-0

## (56)

▷ I. Cheparinov (2685)
► U. Atakisi (2330)
European Championship, 12.05.2016

46.♖d8+! ♔g7 [46...♖f8 47.♕g3++-]
47.♕g3+! ♖g6 [47...♔h6 48.♖d4!+-;
47...♔f7 48.♕c7+! ♔g6 49.♖g8+!+-]
48.♕c7+! ♔h6 49.♕f4+! ♔h5
[49...♕g5 50.♕f8+ ♖g7 51.♖d6+
♔h5 52.♕f3+ ♔h4 53.♖d4++-]
50.g4+! ♔h4 51.g5+ ♔xh3 [51...♔h5
52.♕g4#] 52.♕f3+ ♔h4 53.♖d4+
♔xg5 54.♕f4+ 1-0 [54.♕f4+ ♔h5
55.♕h4#]

## (57)

▷ M. Petrosyan (2480)
► H. Gabuzyan (2620)
European Championship, 13.05.2016

25.♖xd6!! ♖g8 [25...exd6
26.♗xf6++-] 26.♖xd7!! ♖xg5

27.fxg5+- ♕e6 28.gxf6! ♕xe3+ [28...
♕xd7 29.f7+ e5 30.♗xc6+-] 29.♔h1
e5 30.f7 ♖f8 31.♗a3+-

## (58)

▷ R. Edouard (2641)
► T. Stremavicius (2443)
Llucmajor Open, 14.05.2016

16.♘d1!! ♕xa1 17.♕g6!+- ♗xe5
18.♕xg8+ ♔d7 19.♕xa8 ♗xf4
20.exf4+-

## (59)

▷ V. Asadli (2397)
► Y. Kuzubov (2632)
Nakhchivan Open, 14.05.2016

25...♕g7!! [25...♕c5! 26.♕f6 ♖f4!-+]
26.♗c2 ♖d2! 0–1 [26...♖d2 27.♖c1
♕b2-+]

## (60)

▷ D. Navara (2735)
► Z. Sturua (2548)
European Championship, 15.05.2016

20.♘xg6!! [20.♖e1? ♘f2!!-+]
20...♕g5 [20...fxg6 21.♖e1+- ♘f2
22.♕xg6+ ♕g7 23.♖xe8++-] 21.♖xe4
♖xe4 22.♕xe4 ♕xg6 23.♕e2+-

## (61)

▷ D. Nisipeanu (2669)
► D. Khismatullin (2609)
European Championship, 22.05.2016

20.♗xd5! ♗xd4 21.♘xe6!! ♘e5 [21...
fxe6 22.♖xe6 ♖xf3 23.♖xe7+ ♔f8
24.♗xf3 ♔xe7 25.cxd4±] 22.♖xe5!
♗xe5 23.♘xf8 ♖xf8 24.♖e1+-

## (62)

▷ D. Khismatullin (2609)
► D. Yudin (2530)
Kurnosov memorial, 26.05.2016

26.♕xd5!! ♘xd5 27.♖a8+ ♔c7 [27...
♔b7 28.♗xd5+ ♔b6 29.♗e3+ ♔c7
30.♖a7++-] 28.♖a7+ ♔d8 29.♖xd7+
♔xd7 30.♗xd5+-

## (63)

▷ R. Shcherbakov (2492)
► V. Gunina (2497)
Kurnosov memorial, 27.05.2016

17.♘f6!! ♔g7 [17...♘xf6 18.♗xh6+
♔g8 19.♕xe7+-; 17...♗xf6 18.♕xf7#;
17...♖xd7 18.♘xd7+ ♔g7 19.♘xb6+-]
18.♗xh6+! ♘xh6 [18...♔xh6
19.♘xg8+! ♖hxg8 20.♕xe7+-]
19.♕xe7+-

## (64)

▷ P. Potapov (2485)
► P. Maletin (2580)
Kurnosov memorial, 27.05.2016

34...♖e7!! 35.♕c3 [35.♔xf1 ♕b1+-
+; 35.♕c1 ♘xg3 36.fxg3 ♕xg3-+
37.♖xh5+ ♔g6 38.♖b5 ♖e1+; 35.♕f5
♕xf5 36.♖xf5 ♖e1-+] 35...♕b1
36.♖xh5+ ♔g6-+

## (65)

▷ Le Quang Liem (2718)
► M. Kazhgaleyev (2582)
Asian Continental, 28.05.2016

21.♗xg7!! ♔xg7 22.♕b2+ f6
23.♖g3+ ♔h8 24.♖a3!+-

## (66)

▷ R. Kasimdzhanov (2703)
► B. Lalith (2579)
Asian Continental, 29.05.2016

33...Ne3+? [33...Nf4+! 34.Kh2 Nxe6 35.Qxe6 Rg5=] 34.Kf3!! [34.fxe3 Rxe4! 35.Qe8+ Kh7 36.Rxe4 Qc2+ 37.Kf3 Qd1+=] 34...Qd1+ 35.Kxe3 Qe1+ 36.Kf3 1-0

## (67)

▷ M. Kravtsiv (2641)
► G. Szabo (2548)
Zalakaros Open, 04.06.2016

20.Be3!! Nxh1 [20...Qb8 21.Qa5!+-; 20...b5 21.Qa8+ Qb8 22.Qa5 Nxh1 23.0-0-0+-] 21.Bb6! Qb8 22.Qa5! Ng3 23.Qc5+ Bc6 24.Ba6!+- Kd7 25.Rd1+ Ke8 26.Rd8+ Qxd8 27.Bxd8+- Nf5 [27...Kxd8 28.Qd6+ Ke8 29.Qb8++-] 28.Bg5 Rxh7 29.Bxb7 Bxb7 30.Qb5+ Kf8 31.Qxb7 1-0

## (68)

▷ L. Fressinet (2687)
► M. Carlsen (2855)
Grand tour, Paris rapid, 10.06.2016

61...e4? [61...h5!!-+ 62.Bc8 a) 62.Bd7 Rd2 63.Bc6 Rd3+ 64.Bf3 e4-+; b) 62.Nd6 Rd2! 63.Ne4 (63.Nf5 Rd3+-+) 63...Rd3#; c) 62.Ng7 Rg2+ 63.Kf3 Rxg7-+; d) 62.Ne3 e4 63.Bf5 Rf3#; e) 62.Ne7 e4 63.Nf5 Rf3#; 62...Rc2! 63.Be6 Rc3+-+] 62.h5 Rf3+ 63.Kg4 Ra3 64.Kf4=

## (69)

▷ M. Vachier Lagrave (2789)
► V. Anand (2770)
GCT Rapid, 17.06.2016

26...Nxf2!! 27.Kxf2 Qh2+ 28.Ke3 [28.Kf1 Nh4-+] 28...Qg2! 29.Qe2 [29.Rf1 Ne5!! 30.Qe2 Rxf3+! 31.Rxf3 Bxd4+! 32.Kd2 (32.Kxd4 Qxe2-+) 32...Nxf3+-+] 29...Rxf3+! 30.Qxf3 Bxd4+ 31.Kxd4 Qxf3-+

## (70)

▷ D. Navara (2744)
► M. Bartel (2640)
Lublin, 17.06.2016

40.Re7! Nxc4 41.f7 Nd6 42.Re6! 1-0 [42.Re5!+-; 42.Re6! Nxf7 43.gxf7 Rf8 44.Re8+-; 42.Rd7? Nxf7! 43.gxf7 Rf8]

## (71)

▷ J. Tomczak (2588)
► D. Navara (2744)
Lublin, 18.06.2016

31...Bc2!! 32.Qxc2 Qg7+! 33.Kh2 Rxf4-+ 0-1

## (72)

▷ A. Shirov (2682)
► R. Wang (2341)
Edmonton, 18.06.2016

22.Rxb5!! Qxa3 [22...axb5 23.Nxb5 Qc2 24.Nd6+ Kd8 25.Qxf7+-] 23.Rb7! Qf8 24.Qd3! 1-0

## [73]

▷ D. Andreikin (2743)
► A. Volokitin (2624)
Eurasian Blitz Championship,
18.06.2016

**20.♘c6+!** 1–0 [20.♘c6+ ♚c7
21.♖xa8 ♘xe1 (21...♚xc6 22.♚xc2+-)
22.♘xe5 ♘xg2 23.♘c4+!! ♚c6 (23...e5
24.♗g5 ♕e6 25.♗d8+! ♚c6 26.♘a5+
♚d6 27.♘xb7+ ♚c6 28.♘a5+ ♚d6
29.♖a6++-) 24.♖a6+!! bxa6 25.♘a5+
♚b5 26.♕b8+ ♕b6 (26...♚xa5
27.♕b4#) 27.c4+ ♚xa5 (27...♚c5
28.♗a3++-) 28.♗d2++-]

## [74]

▷ W. So (2770)
► F. Caruana (2804)
Grand tour, Leuven blitz, 19.06.2016

**33.♕xg7+!** ♕xg7 34.♖xg7+ ♚xg7
35.♘e2+! ♗e5 36.♘g3! ♖g5 37.♘f3?
[37.f4 ♖xg3 38.fxe5+-; 37.♗xe5+
♖xe5 38.♘g4+-] **37...♗xb2 38.♘xg5**
♗xa3+- [38...♗c1!∞]

## [75]

▷ V. Moiseenko (2497)
► E. Romanov (2642)
Russian Higher league, 22.06.2016

**32...g5!! 33.♖h5** [33.f4 ♘f3+! 34.♖xf3
♕d4+ 35.♖f2 gxh4-+] **33...♘xf3+!**
**34.♖xf3 ♗g4 35.♖xh6 ♖xh6-+**

## [76]

▷ R. Wojtaszek (2729)
► B. Heberla (2541)
Polish league, 24.06.2016

**28.f4!** [28.♕xc7? ♗h3! 29.♗f1 ♖xd4!
30.♖xd4 ♘xf3+] **28...♕xf4 29.♘e6!**
**fxe6** [29...♗xe6 30.♖xd8+-] **30.♖xd8**
**♕f2+ 31.♚h1** 1–0 [31.♚h1 ♕xe2
32.♕xe5+-]

## [77]

▷ Wen Yang (2614)
► E. Inarkiev (2729)
Chinese league, 25.06.2016

**20...♖h3!! 21.♖xh3** [21.♘e3 ♘f4+!!
22.gxf4 exf4 23.♕xg4 (23.♘xg4
f3+! 24.♘xf3 ♕xg4+-+) 23...♕xg4+
24.♘xg4 ♖xd3 25.♘f3 ♖g8-+
26.♖h4 f5 27.exf5 ♗xd5] **21...♘f4+!!**
**22.gxf4 gxh3+ 23.♚f1** [23.♚xh3
♖h8+-+] **23...h2! 24.♕f3 ♕g1+**
**25.♚e2 ♕xa1-+**

## [78]

▷ A. Naiditsch (2657)
► J. Borisek (2576)
Vidmar memorial, 27.06.2016

**25.h5?** [25.♕xe6!! ♖xe6 26.♘xe6 ♘e5
(26...♕xe6 27.♖xf8#) 27.♖xf7 ♖xf7
28.♘f4±] **25...h6∞**

## [79]

▷ Z. Kozul (2594)
► A. Beliavsky (2603)
Vidmar memorial, 28.06.2016

**24.♘hf5?** [24.♘xg6! fxg6 (24...
♕xc1+ 25.♚g2 ♕xh1+ 26.♕xh1
fxg6 27.♗b5+-) 25.♕h7+ ♚f8 (25...
♚f7 26.♕xg6+!! ♚xg6 27.♗h5+
♚h7 28.♗f7++-) 26.♕xg6! ♕xc1+
27.♚g2 ♕c8 (27...♕xe3 28.♖h8+ ♚e7
29.♘f5+! ♚d8 (29...♗xf5 30.♕xe8#)

30.♘xe3+-) 28.♗h5+-] **24...♗xf5**
**25.♘xf5 ♘g3+!** [25...♕xc1+ 26.♔g2
♕xh1+ 27.♔xh1±] **26.♕xg3 ♕xc1+**
**27.♕e1 ♕xe1+ 28.♔xe1 ♗c5=**

## [80]

▷ A. Gabrielian (2520)
► A. Esipenko (2471)
Russian Higher league, 29.06.2016

**48.g6!!** ♕h1+ **49.♔g4** ♕xh6
**50.♕h7!!** 1–0 [50.♕h7 ♕f8 51.g7+-]

## [81]

▷ A. Areshchenko (2654)
► N. Grandelius (2643)
Porticcio Open, 29.06.2016

**40.♕f5!!** gxf6 [40...g6 41.♘d7+ ♔g8
42.♕d5! ♘b6 43.♘f6+ ♔f8 44.♕e5+-
♕d2 45.♘d5!+-] **41.♕xf6! ♔g8**
**42.♘c3! ♖d3 43.♘e7! ♕a1+ 44.♔h2**
♖f8 **45.♘e4!** ♘e5 [45...♕xc3 46.♖g4+
♔h7 47.♖g7+ ♔h8 48.♕xh6#]
**46.♖xd3** 1–0

## [82]

▷ S. Bilguun (2419)
► K. Dragun (2623)
Najdorf memorial, 12.07.2016

**28.♘xg7!!** ♖e7 [28...♔xg7 29.♕h5
♖f7 (29...♖h8 30.♖xf6! ♔xf6 31.♖f1+
♔e7 32.♕f7+ ♔d8 33.♖d1++-) 30.g4!!
(30.♖xf6 ♖xf6 31.♕xe8 ♗e6∞) 30...
♔f8 31.g5+-; 28...♗xg7 29.♕h5 h6
30.♕g6+-] **29.♘h5+-**

## [83]

▷ S. Fedorchuk (2624)
► J. Moussard (2521)
Paris, 16.07.2016

**18...f4! 19.♕f2** [19.♕xf4 ♕xb6–+]
**19...♕f6!! 20.c4** [20.♘xc8 ♕xb2+
21.♔d2 ♗d4 22.♘e7+ ♔g7 23.♕h4
♕c3+! 24.♔c1 ♕a1+! 25.♔d2 ♗c3+
26.♔e2 ♗b5+ 27.♔f2 (27.♖d3
♕xh1–+) 27...♗d4+ 28.♔e1 ♕c3+
29.♖d2 ♗e3–+; 20.♘xd7 ♕xb2+
21.♔d2 ♗d4! 22.♕h4 ♖xc2+!
23.♗xc2 ♖c8 24.♖c1 ♗e3+ 25.♔e2
♗xc1 26.♘f6+ ♔g7–+] **20...bxc3**
**21.♘xd7 cxb2+ 22.♔d2** [22.♔b1
♖c1+! 23.♖xc1 bxc1♕+ 24.♖xc1 ♕a1+
25.♔c2 ♖c8+ 26.♘c5 ♕b2+-+] **22...**
**♕c3+** [22...♕g5! 23.♗d5 (23.♘xf8
♕a5+ 24.♔e2 ♕b5+ 25.♖d3 (25.
♔d2 ♗c3+-+) 25...♖c3-+) 23...♖fd8
24.♘b6 ♗d4!! 25.♕xd4 ♖xg2+-+]
**23.♔e2** Puzzle 84 in HARD Section.

## [84]

▷ S. Fedorchuk (2624)
► J. Moussard (2521)
Paris, 16.07.2016

**23...♕c6!! 24.♘xf8** [24.♕a7 ♖a8
25.♕b6 ♕xd7 26.♖xd6 ♕e7-+] **24...**
**♕b5+ 25.♖d3** [25.♔d2 ♗c3+-+] **25...**
**♖c3! 26.♗xf7+ ♔xf8** 0–1

## [85]

▷ A. Firouzja (2481)
► A. Dreev (2664)
Stars Cup, 18.07.2016

**27...♗d2!! 28.♘xd2** [28.♗xd2 ♕c2+
29.♔a1 ♕xb2#; 28.♕xd2 ♕xe4

29.♔a1 ♘b4–+; 28.♖xd2 ♕xc1+
29.♖xc1 ♖xc1#] 28...♕c2+ 29.♔a1
♖b5! 30.b3 ♖a5 31.a4 ♘b4 0–1

## [86]

▷ **Ding Liren (2778)**
► **A. Grischuk (2747)**
Wenzhou match, 21.07.2016

**28.♖d3?** [28.g4!! ♕xg4 (28...♘f6
29.g5+–; 28...♘g7 29.g5+–) 29.♖d3!
♕e6 30.♗xe5+! ♔g8 31.♖xd6 ♖xd6
32.♗xd6 ♖d8 33.e5+–] **28...♗b5!**
**29.♗xe5+ ♔g8 30.♖xd6 fxg3!∞**

## [87]

▷ **V. Bologan (2654)**
► **A. Korobov (2656)**
Poikovsky, 24.07.2016

**24.♖f1??** [24.♖e1! ♗d4+ (24...♗xd6
25.cxd6 ♕b6+ 26.♕xb6 axb6 27.♖e8#;
24...♘d7 25.♗xf7++–) 25.♗e3! ♗xe3+
(25...♕e7 26.♗e6! ♗xe3+ 27.♖xe3+–)
26.♕xe3! ♘d7 27.♕e7 ♖af8 28.♖f1+–]
**24...♗xd6 0–1** [24...♗xd6 25.cxd6
♕b6+! 26.♕xb6 axb6–+]

## [88]

▷ **E. Zanan (2450)**
► **V. Laznicka (2654)**
Pardubice, 25.07.2016

**32...♘xf2!!** 33.♔xf2 ♕h2 34.♖e1 [34.
♕f3 ♖e3! 35.♕f5 ♖de8–+; 34.♕f5 d3!
35.♖xd3 (35.♘c3 ♖d4–+) 35...♖xd3
36.♕xd3 ♖f6+ 37.♔e3 ♕e5+–+] **34...**
**♖f6+ 35.♔e2 ♖e8+ 0–1**

## [89]

▷ **Wang Chen (2514)**
► **Ding Liren (2777)**
Chinese league, 25.07.2016

**25.♘g5+!! ♕xg5 26.♖xe7+!! ♔xe7**
**27.♕xb7+ ♔d6** [27...♔d8 28.♘e6++–;
27...♔e8 28.♕xc8++–] **28.♗a3+! ♖c5**
**29.♕c6+! 1–0**

## [90]

▷ **R. Mamedov (2666)**
► **E. Demircioglu (2206)**
Turkish league, 25.07.2016

**22.♘d5!! 1–0** [22.♘d5 ♕xd5 (22...gxh5
23.♘xe7#) 23.♕xh7+ ♔xh7 24.♗h3+
♔g8 25.♖h8#]

## [91]

▷ **N. Georgiadis (2470)**
► **B. Bok (2613)**
Biel, 26.07.2016

**47...♖xg1+! 48.♔xg1 ♕e1+ 49.♗f1**
**♕e3+! 50.♔h1** [50.♔g2 ♕g3+ 51.♔h1
♕h2#] **50...♕f3+! 0–1** [50...♕f3+
51.♗g2 ♕d1+–+]

## [92]

▷ **B. Amin (2654)**
► **E. Zude (2403)**
Xtracon Open, 27.07.2016

**22.♗xd5!! ♕xd5+** [22...♘xd5
23.♖fg4+–] **23.♘e4! ♔h8** [23...♘xe4
24.dxe4 ♕e5 25.f6+–] **24.♖xg7! ♖g8**
[24...♔xg7 25.♕xf6+ ♔g8 26.♖g4#]
**25.♖xg8+ ♘xg8 26.f6+–**

## [93]

▷ A. Shirov (2674)
► J. Timman (2559)
Xtracon Open, 29.07.2016

**22.c5!!** 1–0 [22.c5 dxe5 (22...bxc5 23.Qxe6+ Kh8 24.Ng6+ Kh7 25.Qxf5+-) 23.cxb6 Qb7 (23...Qd6 24.b7+-) 24.Rc7 Qd5 25.Qxd5 exd5 26.b7+-]

## [94]

▷ A. Donchenko (2583)
► M. Bartel (2649)
Biel Open, 29.07.2016

**23...Nxe4!! 24.fxe4 Qxe4+ 25.Qd3** [25.Bd3 Qe5 26.b3 Bf6-+; 25.Ka1 Rxb2! 26.Kxb2 Qc2+ 27.Ka1 Bf6+-+] **25...Qe5! 26.Bc3 Rxc3 27.Qd4 Qxe2! 28.Qxc3 Bf6 29.Rd4 Bxd4 30.Qxd4 e5** 0–1 [30...e5 31.Qc3 Qe4+-+]

## [95]

▷ D. Jakovenko (2712)
► V. Bologan (2654)
Poikovsky, 30.07.2016

**15.Bg5!!+-** Qd6 [15...Bxg5 16.Bb5! Qe6 17.Nxg5+- Rxd1+ 18.Rxd1 Qe5 19.Qd3+-] **16.Bb5! Qc7 17.Rxd8+ Kxd8 18.Rd1+ Ke8** [18...Kc8 19.Qf5+ Kb8 20.Bf4+-] **19.Qe4+-**

## [96]

▷ R. Panjwani (2388)
► L. Bruzon (2643)
Calgary Open, 31.07.2016

**25.Ba3!! Qxa3 26.Nxg6! hxg6 27.Qxc7+- Qb4 28.Re8! Ba6 29.a4 Bxb5 30.axb5 Qxb3 31.g3 Qxb5 32.Qxb8+-**

## [97]

▷ S. Mamedyarov (2764)
► B. Savchenko (2633)
Turkish league, 02.08.2016

**20.Nxe7! Nxe7** [20...Bxc4 21.Nxc8+-] **21.Bb5+ Kd6 22.Rc7!! Rxc7 23.Bg3+ Kd5 24.Bxc7+- Bf6** [24...Nf5 25.Bc4+ Ke4 26.f3#] **25.Bc4+** [25.f3+-] **25...Ke4 26.Bd3+ Kd5 27.e4+! Kxd4 28.f4!** 1–0

## [98]

▷ V. Topalov (2761)
► P. Svidler (2751)
Sinquefield Cup, 05.08.2016

**26.Qc3! Nxd4 27.Qxb4! Ne2+** [27...Nxf3+ 28.Kh1+-] **28.Kh1** 1–0 [28.Kh1 Nxc1 29.Qb8+ Kh7 (29...Kf7 30.Qxc7+ Kf6 31.Qxc1+-) 30.Qb1+ Nd3 31.Ne1!+-]

## [99]

▷ E. Cordova (2627)
► J. Sylvan (2342)
Badalona Open, 07.08.2016

**21.Bxh5! gxh5 22.Rxh5! Nxh5** [22...Nh7 23.Rxd5+-] **23.Qxh5 Be4 24.Nhf5+** [24.Nxf7+ Kg8 25.Nxd8+-] **24...Kg8 25.Qg4 Bxf5 26.Nxf5 Ne6 27.Re1+-**

## [100]

▷ H. Nakamura (2791)
► Ding Liren (2755)
Sinquefield Cup, 14.08.2016

**22.♘d5!! exd5 23.♕c8+! ♔e7
24.♖xa6! ♘xg3** [24...♗g7 25.♕c5+!+–
♔d8 26.♖d6++-] **25.♗xb5+-**

## [101]

▷ F. Olivares (2314)
► K. Sasikiran (2658)
Sants Open, 21.08.2016

**30.♖xh5!! gxh5 31.♕g5+ ♘g6**
[31...♔f8 32.♕h6+ ♔g8 (32...♔e8
33.♕h8++-) 33.♘g5+-] **32.♖xd5!!
exd5 33.♘f6+ ♔g7 34.♘xh5+! ♔h7
35.♗e3!! f5** [35...♕e6 36.♕h6+ ♔g8
37.♕g7#] **36.♘f6+ ♔g7 37.♕h6+
♔f7 38.♕h7+ ♔e6 39.♕xg6+- ♕c6
40.♘xd7+ ♔xd7 41.♕f7+ 1–0**

## [102]

▷ D. Sadzikowski (2551)
► T. Banusz (2616)
Abu Dhabi Open, 23.08.2016

**18.♘de7+!! ♘xe7 19.h4! ♘xf5**
[19...♕f6 20.g5 ♕e5 21.♘xe7+
♔h8 22.♗xe6! ♕g3+ (22...♕xe6
23.♘xc8+-) 23.♔h1 ♕xh4+
24.♔g2+-] **20.hxg5 ♘e3 21.♕e2
♘xf1 22.♗xe6 fxe6 23.♖xf1+-**

## [103]

▷ F. Perez Ponsa (2585)
► N. Georgiadis (2475)
Olympiad, 03.09.2016

**28.♗xd6! ♕f3+ 29.♔g1 ♗b6+
30.♖d4!** 1–0 [30.♖d4 exd4 (30...
♘xd6 31.♕g7#) 31.♕f8#]

## [104]

▷ A. Bachmann (2641)
► J. Gomez (2492)
Olympiad, 03.09.2016

**29.♘xf5!! ♗xf5 30.♗xf5 ♖xf5
31.♖d8+ ♔h7 32.♕e4! g6 33.g4!
♖f6** [33...♖ff7 34.f5!+-] **34.f5! ♕a6
35.♖bd1!+-** [35.fxg6+ ♖xg6 36.♖bd1!
♖eg7 37.h4!+-] **35...gxf5 36.gxf5 ♗d6
37.♖g1 1–0**

## [105]

▷ K. Piorun (2681)
► L. Draskovic (2448)
Olympiad, 05.09.2016

**29.♖xg7!! ♔xg7** [29...bxa3 30.♖hg1!
axb2 31.♖g8+ ♖xg8 32.hxg8♕+
♖xg8 33.♕h6#] **30.♕h6+ ♔h8
31.♗e3!! ♕xe3** [31...♕c7 32.♖g1 ♗g5
33.♗xg5+-] **32.♕xe3+-**

## [106]

▷ C. Lupulescu (2618)
► S. Mamedyarov (2761)
Olympiad, 05.09.2016

**21...♘xe5! 22.f4 ♘f3+!! 23.♔h1** [23.
♕xf3 ♕c5+ 24.♔h1 ♕xd6–+] **23...
♕c5! 24.♕xf3** [24.♘b7 ♕b6∓] **24...
♕xd6∓**

## [107]

▷ A. Shirov (2673)
► R. Rapport (2752)
Olympiad, 06.09.2016

**19.♕f1!!** [19.♘f4 g5!∞] **19... ♗f3** [19...♕xg6 20.e5! ♕xc2 21.♕f7+ ♔d8 22.♕d7#] **20.♖g1+-**

## [108]

▷ **Wang Yue (2737)**
► **S. Mareco (2606)**
Olympiad, 08.09.2016

**34...♖g3+!!  35.fxg3 ♕f1+ 36.♔h2 ♗xg3+!** 0–1 [36...♗xg3+ 37.♔xg3 ♖f3+ 38.♔h4 ♕xh3+ 39.♔g5 ♕h6#]

## [109]

▷ **Li Chao (2746)**
► **Z. Almasi (2684)**
Olympiad, 10.09.2016

**30...♖f5!! 31.c7** [31.♔c2 ♖c5! 32.♕xc5 d3+ 33.♗xd3 ♕xc5+–+] **31...d3 32.♕xd3 ♖xf1+ 33.♔c2 ♖xa1** 0–1

## [110]

▷ **B. Jobava (2665)**
► **R. Ponomariov (2709)**
Olympiad, 10.09.2016

**17.♗h6!! gxh6** [17...♕d8 18.♗xg7!! ♘h5 (18...♕xe7 19.♕g5+-; 18...♔xg7 19.♕g5+ ♔f8 20.♗xf6 ♕xe7 21.♕h8#) 19.♗f6! ♘xf6 20.♕g5+ ♔f8 21.♕xf6 ♕xe7 22.♕h8#; 17...♘c6 18.♗xg7! ♘h5 a) 18...♘xe7 19.♗xf6 ♔f8 (19... ♘g6 20.♕h6+-) 20.♕h6+ ♔e8 21.♗xe7 ♔xe7 22.♘xd5+! ♗xd5 23.♕xb6+-; b) 18...♔xg7 19.♕g5+ ♔f8 20.♖xe6 fxe6 21.♕xf6+ ♔g8 22.♕xe6+ ♔g7 23.♕xf5+-; 19.♗f6!! ♘xe7 20.♗xe7+- f6 21.♕h6 ♕c7 22.♖e1! ♕xe7 23.♗xf5 ♖c6 24.♕xh5+-; 17...♕xd4 18.♕g5+-]

**18.♕xh6 ♖xc3** [18...♗d7 19.♖de1! ♕xd4 20.♖1e3+-; 18...♘c6 19.♕g5+! ♔f8 20.♖xe6 fxe6 21.♕xf6+ ♔g8 22.♕xe6+ ♔g7 23.♕xf5+-] **19.♕g5+ ♔f8 20.♕xf6 ♖xd3 21.cxd3** 1–0

## [111]

▷ **J. Gomez (2492)**
► **F. Perez Ponsa (2585)**
Olympiad, 11.09.2016

**26...♗e7! 27.♕xe5 ♗f8! 28.♕d5 ♕xb6–+**

## [112]

▷ **D. Nisipeanu (2687)**
► **A. Volodin (2473)**
Olympiad, 13.09.2016

**29.♖e1!! ♖c8** [29...fxg3 30.♖e8+ ♔c7 31.♖xh8 g2 32.♘f3! g1♕+ 33.♘xg1 ♖xg1+ 34.♔d2+-] **30.♗f3** [30.♖e8 ♖f6 31.♗f3+-] **30...♖f6** [30...♖xg5 31.♖xf4+-] **31.♖e7+-**

## [113]

▷ **N. Tutisani (2375)**
► **L. Pantsulaia (2601)**
Georgian league, 22.09.2016

**30...♗xg2+! 31.♔xg2 ♕g4+ 32.♔h1 ♕f3+ 33.♔g1 ♗c5+! 34.♖e3** [34.♗e3 ♖b4!–+] **34...♖b4!–+**

## [114]

▷ **M. Parligras (2595)**
► **D. Solak (2635)**
Serbian league, 22.09.2016

**33...♘xe4!! 34.♘xe4** [34.♗xb4 ♗xb4+ 35.♔e2 ♘xf2!–+] **34...♕xe4+**

35.♕e2 ♕g6–+ [35...♘c2+ 36.♔d1
♕d4! 37.♖xc2 ♖a1+ 38.♖c1 ♖xc1+
39.♔xc1 ♗a3+! 40.♔d1 ♕a1+]

## (115)

▷ **Zhang Zhong (2634)**
► **X. Xu (2447)**
Chinese league, 24.09.2016

31.♖xe6+! fxe6 32.♕e5 ♕d2+
33.♔b1 ♔f7 [33...♕xd3+ 34.♔a1
♕xf5 35.♖g7+ ♔f8 36.♘h7+ ♕xh7
37.♕f6#] 34.♖g7+! 1–0 [34.♖g7+
♔xg7 35.♘h5+ ♔f7 36.♕g7#]

## (116)

▷ **L. Van Wely (2674)**
► **E. Iturrizaga (2650)**
Spanish league, 26.09.2016

37.♖xe4! gxf2+ 38.♖g4! f1♕+
39.♖xf1! ♕d2+ [39...♖d2+ 40.♔h1
♕h5 41.♕f4++-] 40.♔g1! ♕e3+
41.♖f2! 1–0

## (117)

▷ **D. Anton Guijjaro (2630)**
► **T. Banusz (2613)**
Spanish league, 26.09.2016

30.♖e3!! ♕a3+ 31.♔b1 h5 32.♖e8+
♔h7 33.♕e4+ 1–0 [33.♕e4+ g6
34.♖e7++-]

## (118)

▷ **A. Naiditsch (2684)**
► **A. Gupta (2626)**
Isle of Man, 04.10.2016

33.♗f4?∞ [33.♗xd6!! cxd6 34.g4!!+-
(34.c7 ♕f5) ]

## (119)

▷ **J. Granda Zuniga (2648)**
► **W. So (2794)**
Isle of Man, 04.10.2016

23...a3!! 24.♘c2 [24.♖xb6 ♖b2!
25.♖xb2 (25.♖b3 a2–+) 25...axb2–+]
24...♗d6 25.♖c3 ♘a4 26.♖c4
♗e6–+

## (120)

▷ **S. Tiviakov (2590)**
► **T. Kotanjian (2473)**
Yerevan Open, 10.10.2016

24.♕b5! ♕xb5 25.♖xc8+ ♗f8
26.♗h6 ♘d7 27.♖xe7! ♕c5 [27...♖c4
28.♖d8!+-] 28.♖xf8+! 1–0 [28.♖xf8+
♘xf8 29.♖e8+-]

## (121)

▷ **A. Markgraf (2523)**
► **A. Braun (2579)**
German league, 16.10.2016

22...♘d4!! 23.g3 [23.♗xd3 ♘df3+
24.gxf3 ♘xf3+ 25.♔f1 ♕xa4–+;
23.♖xd3 ♘xd3 24.♕xd4 ♕xd4
25.♘xd4 ♘xe1–+; 23.♘xd4 ♖xd4
24.♕b3 axb5–+] 23...♘df3+ 24.♔f1
♕xa4 25.♗xa4 ♘xe1–+

## (122)

▷ **K. Sychev (2445)**
► **B. Savchenko (2613)**
Moscow league, 23.10.2016

19.♖xd5! ♘xd5 20.♕xh7+ ♔f8
21.♘xf7!! ♕d7 [21...♔xf7 22.♗h6
♖g8 23.♖d1+-] 22.♘e5+- [22.
♗d6++-]

## (123)

▷ A. Moiseenko (2648)
► T. Radjabov (2710)
Corsican Circuit, 28.10.2016

17... ♗f4!! 18. ♗xc8 ♗xh2+! 19.♔xh2
♘f4 20. ♗xd7 [20. ♕e4 ♕h4–+] 20...
♕h4 21. ♗xe6 fxe6 0–1

## (124)

▷ V. Zvjagintsev (2675)
► D. Schwarz (2278)
European Club Cup, 06.11.2016

44.♖xa6!! bxa6 45.b7 ♕d8 [45...
♕c7 46.♘e8++-] 46.♕xh6+!! ♔xh6
47.♘xf7+ 1–0 [47.♘xf7+ ♔h7
48.♘xd8+-]

## (125)

▷ E. Blomqvist (2552)
► C. Noe (2422)
European Club Cup, 06.11.2016

29...♕xf1+! 30.♔xf1 ♖xf2+ 31.♔g1
[31.♔e1 d2+!–+] 31...♖fd2!–+ 32.♗e2
♖xe2 33.♔f1 ♖cd2 0–1

## (126)

▷ P. Harikrishna (2768)
► M. Bluebaum (2641)
European Club Cup, 09.11.2016

23.♘xd5!! ♕c5 [23...♗xd5 24.♕g3!
g6 25.♘xh6+ ♔g7 26.♘xf7! ♗xf7
27.♖xf7+ ♔xf7 28.♕xg6+ ♔e7
29.♕g5+!+- ♔e8 (29...♔e6 30.♗f5+
♔d5 31.♖d1+ ♔c5 32.♕e3+ ♔b5
33.♗d3+ ♔a5 34.♖a1++-) 30.♗g6+
♔f8 31.♖f1++-] 24.♘fe7+! ♘xe7

25.♘xe7+ ♔h8 [25...♕xe7 26.♕xa7+-]
26.♘c6! ♕xc6 27.♕xa7+-

## (127)

▷ V. Fedoseev (2673)
► M. Perunovic (2616)
European Club Cup, 09.11.2016

25.♖c6!! ♗xc6 26.d6+! ♔h8 [26...♖f7
27.♗xf7+ ♕xf7 (27...♔xf7 28.♖xc6!
♖xc6 29.♕d5+ ♔f6 30.♕xc6+-)
28.♖xc6!! ♖xc6 29.d7+-] 27.dxc7
♕e7 [27...♖xc7 28.♗b5!+-] 28.♕c3
h6 [28...♖xc7 29.♗b5+-] 29.♗f1+-
[29.♕e5! ♖xc7 30.♗d5+-]

## (128)

▷ L. Dominguez Perez (2752)
► D. Andreikin (2736)
European Club Cup, 10.11.2016

39...♕a5! 40.a4 ♘d5!! 41.exd5 ♖xd2
42.♖xd2 ♖xf1+ 43.♔a2 [43.♔b2
♕xd5∓] 43...♗xd5!∓

## (129)

▷ F. Caruana (2823)
► H. Nakamura (2779)
Champions Showdown Rapid,
10.11.2016

33.♘f5+! ♔e6 34.♕f8! ♕d8 [34...
♖xc1 35.♘g7#] 35.♕xc5! ♗b6 [35...
♖xc1 36.♕c6++-] 36.♕c6+ ♖d6
37.♘xd6 [37.♕xa4±] 37...♕xd6
38.♕e8+ ♕e7 39.♕xa4±

## (130)

▷ **H. Nakamura (2779)**
▶ **V. Topalov (2760)**
Champions Showdown Rapid,
11.11.2016

**11.♗xb8! ♘xc3** [11...♗xc3+ 12.bxc3
♖xb8 13.f3! ♘g3 14.♕a4+ ♗d7
15.♕d4!+-] **12.♕xf5 ♘e4+ 13.♔e2
♕xb8** [13...♖xb8 14.♕e5++-]
**14.♕xd5** 1-0

## (131)

▷ **V. Mikhalevski (2508)**
▶ **Bu Xiangzhi (2698)**
European Club Cup, 11.11.2016

**30...♖d1!! 31.♖xd1** [31.♕xc3 ♕xc3
32.♖xc3 ♖xa1-+] **31...♘xd1 32.♖c1
♕f6! 33.f4** [33.f3 ♕h4-+] **33...♕h4-+**

## (132)

▷ **V. Topalov (2760)**
▶ **H. Nakamura (2779)**
Champions Showdown, 12.11.2016

**29.♕h2!! ♗xg4 30.♖e5 ♗f5 31.g4!+-**

## (133)

▷ **F. Caruana (2823)**
▶ **V. Topalov (2760)**
Champions Showdown Blitz,
14.11.2016

**35.♗e6!! ♖f8** [35...♖xd1 36.♕e8+
♔h7 37.♕g8+ ♔g6 38.♗f5+ ♔h5
39.♕h7! ♕e8 40.♗g4+ ♔xg4
41.♕f5#] **36.♗f5+-**

## (134)

▷ **A. Chandra (2509)**
▶ **B. Finegold (2493)**
Saint Louis, 18.11.2016

**31.♖f5!! ♖e1+** [31...gxf5 32.♖g1+-]
**32.♖xe1 gxf5 33.♗f3+-** 1-0

## (135)

▷ **J. Sriram (2426)**
▶ **M. Karthikeyan (2530)**
Indian Championship, 24.11.2016

**22...♘xf4!! 23.♗xf4** [23.♖xf4 ♗xf4
24.♗xf4 ♕xe1+-+] **23...♗xf4!
24.♕xf4** [24.♖xe7 ♗xd2-+] **24...
♕xe1! 25.♖xe1 ♖xe1+ 26.♔f2 ♖f1+!
27.♔xf1 ♗d3+ 28.♔f2 ♖xf4+ 29.♔e3
♖d4!-+**

## (136)

▷ **J. Glud (2506)**
▶ **H. Ziska (2551)**
Runavik Open, 24.11.2016

**28...♖xe5! 29.fxe5 ♗xe5+ 30.♗f4**
[30.♔g1 ♖c8!-+] **30...♗xf4+ 31.♖xf4
♖c8! 32.♕xd4 ♘xf4 33.♕xf4 ♖c2+
34.♔g3 ♖g2+ 35.♔h4 ♕e7+ 36.♕g5**
[36.g5 h6-+] **36...♕d6-+**

## (137)

▷ **V. Fedoseev (2673)**
▶ **A. Goganov (2643)**
Governor's Cup, 24.11.2016

**37.♕h5+! ♔g8 38.♕d1!+-** 1-0

## (138)

▷ J. Radlovacki (2328)
► M. Savic (2503)
Belgrade Open, 26.11.2016

**19.d5!! ♘xd5 20. ♗g7! ♖g8 21.♖xd5! ♕xd5 22.♕xd5 exd5 23. ♗xf6+-**

## (139)

▷ V. Hamitevici (2484)
► H. Ziska (2551)
Runavik Open, 26.11.2016

**27... ♗xa2+! 28.♔xa2 b3+! 29.♔xb3 ♕b4+ 30.♔a2 ♖d2 31.♖c8+ ♗f8 32.♖c2 ♖xe2! 33.♖xe2 ♕a4+ 0–1** [33...♕a4+ 34.♔b1 ♕d1+ 35.♔a2 ♕xe2–+]

## (140)

▷ C. Foisor (2360)
► L. Vajda (2597)
Kings Rapid RR, 29.11.2016

**42.d5! ♘xd5 43. ♗b2+ ♔g8** [43...♘c3 44.♖c1+-] **44.♕h4! ♘c3 45.♖f6! 1–0**

## (141)

▷ I. Lysyj (2643)
► M. Demidov (2536)
Russian Rapid Cup, 03.12.2016

**25.♘xg6!! ♖e1+** [25...fxg6 26.♖xf6! ♗xf6 27.♘xd5 ♗xd5 28. ♗xd5+ ♔g7 29. ♗xa8+-] **26.♖xe1 ♕xe1+ 27.♔h2 ♖e8** [27...fxg6 28.♖xf6 ♗xf6 29.♘xd5+-] **28.♘e5+-**

## (142)

▷ M. Vachier Lagrave (2811)
► J. Krassowizkij (2438)
German league, 04.12.2016

**29.e6! ♖xe6 30.♖e1! c5** [30...♕c8 31.♕g4++-] **31.♖xe6 fxe6 32.♕g4+ ♔f8 33.♕g7+ ♔e8 34.♕g8+ ♗f8 35. ♗xc5 1–0**

## (143)

▷ S. Sjugirov (2670)
► S. Yudin (2524)
Russian Cup, 06.12.2016

**27.c5!!** [27. ♗xb4? c5] **27... ♗xc3 28. ♗b3+ ♔g7** [28...♔h8 29.♕xc3+ ♕g7 30.♕xg7+ ♔xg7 31.♖e7+ ♔f6 32.♖xb7+-] **29.♕xc3+ ♔h6** [29...♗f6 30.♖e8+-] **30.cxb6! ♕d8** [30...axb6 31.♕b4! ♕d8 32.♖e7+-; 30...♕xb6 31.♖e7+-] **31.bxa7+-**

## (144)

▷ V. Topalov (2760)
► F. Caruana (2823)
London, 10.12.2016

**36...♖e8!! 37.♖xb7+** [37.♘xb2 ♖xe1+ 38.♔xe1 cxb2 39.g8♕ b1♕+ 40.♔d2 ♕c2+ 41.♔e3 ♕e2+ 42.♔f4 d2; 37.♕xe8 ♕c1+ 38.♕e1 d2–+] **37... ♖xb7 38.♕xe8 ♕b1+ 0–1** [38...♕b1+ 39.♕e1 c2 40.g8♕ ♕xe1+ 41.♔xe1 c1♕#]

## (145)

▷ **K. Arkell (2447)**
► **S. Maze (2608)**
London Open, 11.12.2016

**39.♕d7!! ♘e2+** [39...♕xb2 40.♕xf7+ ♔h6 41.♕f8+ ♔g5 *(41...♔h5 42.♕h8+ ♔g5 43.♖g3+ ♔f4 44.♕h4+ ♔f5 45.♕g5#)* 42.h4+! ♔h5 *(42...♔g4 43.♗f3++-; 42...♔xh4 43.♕h6+ ♔g4 44.♕xg6++-)* 43.♗f3+ *(43.♕h8+ ♔g4 44.♕h6!+-)* 43...♘xf3+ 44.♕xf3+ ♔h6 45.♕f8+ ♔h5 *(45...♔h7 46.♖f3 ♕d4+ 47.♔h2+-)* 46.♕h8+ ♔g4 47.♕c8+ ♔h5 48.♖g3! ♕d4+ 49.♔g2 ♕e4+ 50.♔h2+-] **40.♔f2 ♘xc3 41.♕xf7+ ♔h6 42.♕f8+ ♔g5 43.h4+!** 1–0 [43.h4+ ♔xh4 44.♕h6+ ♔g4 45.♗e6#]

## (146)

▷ **D. Martins (2382)**
► **A. Gupta (2634)**
London Open, 12.12.2016

**22...♘xf2!! 23.♘xf2** [23.♖xf2 f5! 24.♔h1 ♗xf2 25.♕xf2 fxe4–+] **23...♕xe1! 24.♖xe1 ♖xe1+ 25.♗f1 ♗e3!**–+ 0–1 [25...♗e3 26.♕c3 ♖d2–+]

www.chess-evolution.com

Arkadij Naiditsch
Csaba Balogh

# Best attacking
## games of 2012–2015

Arkadij Naiditsch
Csaba Balogh

# Most instructive
## endgames of 2012–2015

Arkadij Naiditsch
Csaba Balogh

# Most inte
## draws of 20

Arkadij Naiditsch
Csaba Balogh

# Positio
## masterpieces of

Arkadij Naiditsch
Csaba Balogh

# Best fighting
## games of 2012–2015

Caruana vs Gelfand

**33... ♖e3!!**

Carlsen vs Anand

**25. ♘h3!!**

Carlsen vs Li Chao

**24.d5!!**

Chess
Evolution

www.chess-evolution.com

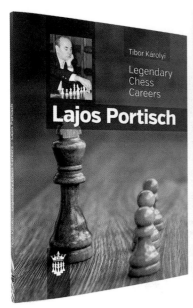

Tibor Károlyi

Legendary
Chess
Careers

# Lajos Portisch

Tibor Károlyi

Legendary
Chess
Careers

# Jan Timman

Tibor Károlyi

Legendary
Chess
Careers

# Eugenio Torre

Tibor Károlyi

Legendary
Chess
Careers

# Vlastimil Hort

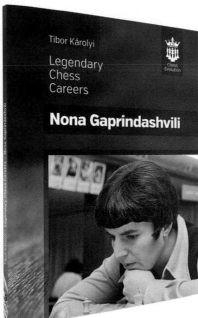

Tibor Károlyi

Legendary
Chess
Careers

# Nona Gaprindashvili

Tibor Károlyi

Legendary
Chess
Careers

# Yasser Seirawan

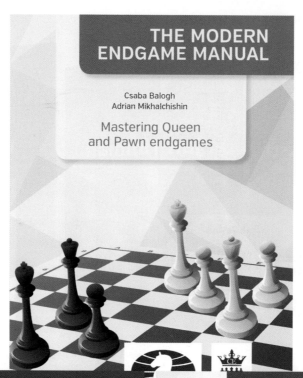

# THE MODERN ENDGAME MANUAL

Csaba Balogh
Adrian Mikhalchishin

## Mastering Queen and Pawn endgames

# THE MODERN ENDGAME MANUAL

Csaba Balogh
Adrian Mikhalchishin

## Mastering minor piece endgames

**1**

# THE MODERN ENDGAME MANUAL

Csaba Balogh
Adrian Mikhalchishin

## Mastering minor piece endgames

**2**

www.chess-evolution.com

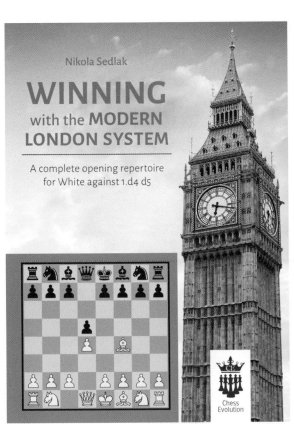

Nikola Sedlak

# WINNING
with the **MODERN LONDON SYSTEM**

A complete opening repertoire
for White against 1.d4 d5

# Complete Slav I
## Konstantin Sakaev

Matthieu Cornette
Fabien Libiszewski

# The complete
# Kalashnikov

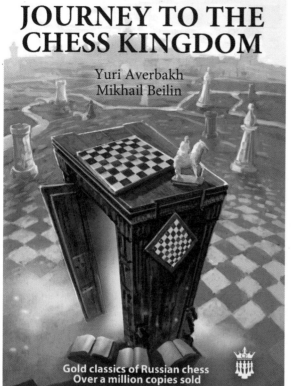

# JOURNEY TO THE CHESS KINGDOM

Yuri Averbakh
Mikhail Beilin

**Gold classics of Russian chess
Over a million copies sold**

Peter Zhdanov

**David
vs
Goliath**

Chess
Evolution

DANIEL GORMALLY

Insanity, passion
and addiction
———
**a year inside
the chess world**

Chess
Evolution

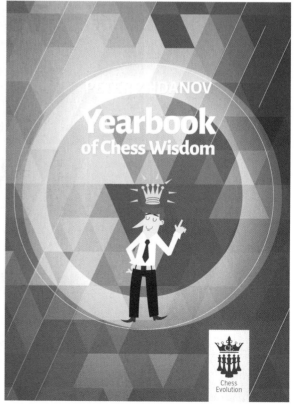

PETER ZHDANOV

**Yearbook
of Chess Wisdom**

Chess
Evolution